Protecting Our Future

Report of the Working Group on Elder Abuse

September 2002

BAILE ÁTHA CLIATH
ARNA FHOILSIÚ AG OIFIG AN tSOLÁTHAIR
Le ceannach díreach ón
OIFIG DHÍOLTA FOILSEACHÁN RIALTAIS,
TEACH SUN ALLIANCE, SRÁID THEACH LAIGHEAN, BAILE ÁTHA CLIATH 2,
nó tríd an bpost ó
FOILSEACHÁIN RIALTAIS, AN RANNÓG POST-TRÁCHTA,
51 FAICHE STIABHNA, BAILE ÁTHA CLIATH 2,
(Teil: 01 - 6476834/35/36/37; Fax: 01 - 6476843)
nó trí aon díoltóir leabhar.

———

DUBLIN
PUBLISHED BY THE STATIONERY OFFICE
To be purchased directly from the
GOVERNMENT PUBLICATIONS SALE OFFICE,
SUN ALLIANCE HOUSE, MOLESWORTH STREET, DUBLIN 2,
or by mail order from
GOVERNMENT PUBLICATIONS, POSTAL TRADE SECTION,
51 ST. STEPHEN'S GREEN, DUBLIN 2,
(Tel: 01 - 6476834/35/36/37; Fax: 01 - 6476843)
or through any bookseller.

———

€4.00

i16994450

Table of Contents

Appendices

Acknowledgements

The Working Group on Elder Abuse is indebted to the following for their help:

- The Chief Executive Officer's of the Southern Health Board, Mr Sean Hurley, and the Mid-Western Health Board, Mr Stiofán de Búrca, and staff of the two pilot project areas of the Southern and Mid-Western Health Boards. Under the leadership of Hilary Scanlon and Irene O'Connor, the pilot projects were carried out in an exceptionally thorough and professional way.

- Ciaran Foley and Rowena Henderson, Henderson-Foley Management Consultants, who undertook the programme of training in an exemplary and flexible manner, despite the exceptionally difficult circumstances created by the foot and mouth crisis.

- Patricia Conboy, whose outstanding analysis of the pilot projects greatly facilitated the work of the Working Group.

- Yvonne McGivern, who provided invaluable skills in report-writing and in enabling this report to be both concise and relevant.

- The helpful philosophy and policies of *No Secrets*, the UK policy on abuse of older and vulnerable adults, which provided a basis for developing policies and procedures for an Irish setting.

- The National Council on Ageing and Older People (NCAOP), for its assistance in the technical support of the Working Group.

- The Law Reform Commission, which aided us in formulating our recommendations on legal issues.

- Women's Aid, which provided us with valuable insights into issues relating to domestic violence in Ireland.

- Professor James O'Brien of Louisville University, USA, whose experience and breadth of knowledge of international trends in elder abuse were invaluable.

- Other groups who provided us with help were the Dementia Services Information and Development Centre, the Criminal Assets Bureau, and the Fraud Squad.

- We also recognise and thank those practitioners whose pioneering work brought elder abuse to the attention of Irish health and social professionals. Their work is referenced in the bibliography.

- Finally we thank those individuals who sent us submissions. These were instrumental in shaping the work and conclusions of the Working Group on Elder Abuse.

Foreword

The Working Group on Elder Abuse is pleased to present this Report. It provides a foundation for the development of policy and procedures to respond to actual or alleged cases of elder abuse.

Aim of policy and procedures

The aim of the policy and procedures presented here is to create a context in which older people and those concerned about the abuse of older people can disclose their concerns and receive an appropriate response. The basis of the policy (and the procedures flowing from it) is the recognition of the right of older people to live independent lives with dignity.

First step

It is important to point out that we see the policy and procedures as representing a minimum change, a first step in tackling the complex issue of elder abuse in Irish society. The resources required to support the initiatives outlined here represent an absolute need. The policy and procedures, however, should not be seen as rigid or prescriptive, but rather as offering a framework for the provision of suitable training and the development and implementation of good practice.

We realise that, as our knowledge of elder abuse and our experience in dealing with it grows, it will be necessary to review both policy and procedures in order to ensure continuing good practice.

Philosophy of approach

In approaching the task set out in the terms of reference, the Working Group agreed that a response to the needs of older people suffering from or at risk of abuse must be formulated within the context of a mainstream system of services for older people, with the principles, policy and professional expertise that such services require. Such a response — comprehensive, integrated and person-centred — has the potential to focus attention on abused older people, to enhance specific services available to them and, where necessary, to devise new approaches to meet their specific or urgent needs.

Constraints on the approach

However, we had to approach the task within the context of current community care services for older people at health board level. While significant advances have been made in some aspects of service provision, we know from research that these community care services are not adequate.

In particular, community social care services — identified by the National Council on Ageing and Older People (NCAOP) as 'core' services, essential to meet the needs of many older people, and particularly important in the prevention of and response to abuse — have not been developed as an adequately resourced, predictably available and effective service system.

Had a mainstream service been in place, responsibility for implementing on a pilot basis our recommendations on policy, procedures and guidelines would have rested with that service, probably with a lesser need for the specific structure we supplied to determine 'who does what'.

However, the evaluation of the pilot programmes showed that the clarification of roles, responsibilities and structures we provided to help with planning, co-ordination, monitoring and accountability worked well in practice and introduced a rigorous scrutiny essential to the process of responding to elder abuse.

The findings from the evaluation of the pilot programmes reinforced our view that the prevention, assessment and management of elder abuse cases should indeed be placed in the context of a mainstream system of services for older people. The findings also served to emphasise the need for adequate health and social care provision: we found that increased health and social care provision was a key element in the effective management of cases of alleged elder abuse.

Going forward

While we set out wanting (but not able) to place the response to elder abuse in the context of an adequate system of services for older people and have found that this is indeed where it should be, such a system does not currently exist. For our recommendations to be effective in addressing elder abuse, it is essential that such a system be put in place. We therefore strongly urge that existing Government policy on the provision of services for older people — *The Years Ahead* and *Quality and Fairness* (including *An Action Plan for Dementia*) — be fully implemented. In addition, urgent attention must be given to the provision of a formal framework to ensure quality of care for older people in both community and residential care.

Structure of the report

The report is divided into three sections: in Section One we present the background to this issue and our recommendations for addressing elder abuse; in Section Two we set out details of the policy and the procedures for responding to instances of elder abuse and the staff structures needed to support them; and in Section Three we present guidance on the prevention of elder abuse.

Our summary includes clear recommendations on:

1. the principles, policy and procedures to be followed in suspected cases of elder abuse

2. the minimum infrastructure, including legislative changes required for these policies to be implemented

3. the timeframe for implementation of these infrastructures and training programmes

4. a mechanism to oversee the implementation of this report, including the Department of Health National Implementation Group

5. a mechanism to promote ongoing substantive research and the incorporation of new research into clinical practice.

The implementation of this report in full and in a timely fashion will enable our society to come to terms with a very real problem, not only for older Irish people of the present generation but also for ourselves as we age.

Professor Desmond O'Neill, MA MD FRCPI
Chairman, Working Group on Elder Abuse
September 2002

Membership of the Working Group on Elder Abuse

Mr. John Brady	Department of Health and Children
Ms. Mary Brennan	Home Help Organiser, Dublin
Mr. Bob Carroll	National Council on Ageing and Older People
Ms. Janet Convery	Director of Services for Older People, East Coast Area Health Board
Dr. Colm Cooney	Consultant in Old Age Psychiatry, St. Vincent's Hospital, Dublin
Ms. Ann Doherty	Matron, Abbeyleix District Hospital, Co. Laois
Ms. Antoinette Doocey	Director of Services for Older People, North-Eastern Health Board
Dr. Joseph Duggan	Consultant Physician in Geriatric Medicine, Mater Hospital, Dublin
Dr. Susan Finnerty	Consultant Psychiatrist, Clare Mental Health Services
Mr. Frank Goodwin	Senior Housing Welfare Officer, Dublin Corporation
Dr. Henry Jack*	Irish College of General Practitioners
Ms. Geraldine Kenny	Principal Clinical Psychologist, Psychology Society of Ireland
Supt. John Mulligan	Garda Síochána Community Relations Section, Dublin
Ms. Niav O'Daly	Representative, Irish Association of Older People
Ms. Anne O'Loughlin**	Senior Social Worker, St. Mary's Hospital, Dublin
Prof. Desmond O'Neill	Professor of Medical Gerontology, Trinity College Dublin **(Chairman)**
Ms. Dolores O'Neill	Director of Public Health Nursing, Western Health Board
Dr. Richard Shanahan***	Irish College of General Practitioners
Ms. Aideen Stanley	Irish Nursing Home Organisation representative

Secretariat

Research Officer:	Ms Deirdre Fitzpatrick
Administrative Officer:	Ms Margaret Flynn

---

* Replaced Dr. Richard Shanahan, Co. Kerry
** Resigned from the Working Group in February 2002
*** Resigned from the Working Group in May 2000

CHAPTER 1

Introduction

Background

1.1 Until relatively recently elder abuse — the abuse, neglect and/or mistreatment of older people — was not recognised as a problem in common with other forms of abuse and maltreatment (O'Neill et al, 1990), (O'Loughlin and Duggan, 1998). A widespread lack of awareness, together with a slowness to accept its existence, was further exacerbated by the 'veil of silence which too often surrounds this phenomenon' (Council of Europe Study Group on Violence against Elderly People, 1992).

1.2 In the last 15 years or so this had begun to change, partly because of the recognition and acceptance of other forms of abuse — child abuse and domestic violence — as social problems. Other factors have also played a part: studies about and reports of elder abuse in professional journals and in the media; developments and deficits in care, as the number of older people rises; and the involvement of professional and advocacy groups with older people.

Size of the problem

1.3 We do not know the prevalence of elder abuse in Ireland but it does happen, and is likely to occur to the same extent as it has in other developed countries: studies show that about three to five per cent of older people living in the community suffer abuse at any one time. This means that in Ireland between 12,000 and 20,000 people living in the community may be suffering from abuse, neglect and/or maltreatment (O'Loughlin and Duggan, 1998). It is important to note that these figures underestimate the size of the problem since we have no figures on the incidence of abuse in institutions, where it also happens.

1.4 We know that the number of people in the Irish population aged 65 and over is growing, and that the number aged 85 and over is growing substantially. It is inevitable, then, that the number of people at risk of and suffering from abuse will increase, while at the same time identification and prevention are likely to be hindered by the prevalence of ageism and the devalued status of older people.

1.5 It is therefore imperative that the issue of elder abuse is tackled at national and local level. To begin the process, in October 1999, the Minister of State at the Department of Health and Children, with special responsibility for older people, established the Working Group on Elder Abuse, following publication of the report *Abuse, Neglect, and Mistreatment of Older People* (O'Loughlin and Duggan, 1998), by the National Council on Ageing and Older People.

1.6   The role of the Working Group is to advise the Minister on what is required to address effectively and sensitively the issue of elder abuse in general, as well as particular incidences of elder abuse. More specifically, it is to make recommendations in relation to each of the following matters:

- Definitions and terminology

- Identification and screening procedures

- Assessment protocols and procedures

- Management of sensitive information

- Recording and reporting procedures

- Inter-agency communications and referral practices

- Intervention mechanisms and procedures to evaluate their impact

- Any necessary changes in legislation and legal procedures

- Training of relevant staff in statutory, voluntary and private sectors

- The need for appropriate structures to deal with elder abuse.

Process

1.7   The Working Group, which met once a month, had a membership of 18, representing a wide range of health and social care professionals and administrators, as well as a representative of the Irish Association of Older People and the Director of the NCAOP. It was chaired by Professor Desmond O'Neill. The Research Officer was Ms Deirdre Fitzpatrick and clerical/administrative support was provided by Ms Margaret Flynn.

1.8   The Working Group instigated a two-year programme of work on which to base its advice. This involved requesting and receiving submissions from interested parties (a summary of the submissions is presented in Appendix A); reviewing international literature and best practice on elder abuse; and attending conferences and seminars. From this accumulated body of knowledge, the Working Group developed training programmes and draft policies, procedures and guidelines to pilot test and evaluate.

1.9   The draft policies, procedures and guidelines were implemented on a pilot basis for a period of six months in two health board areas, the Mid-Western Health Board and the Southern Health Board. Before starting the pilot projects, relevant staff in each area were trained by using the specially developed programmes. Further details of the pilot projects and the training are contained in Appendix B.

1.10   The aim of the pilot projects was twofold:

- to see how the draft policies, procedures and guidelines worked in practice; and

- to determine whether or not there were areas of unmet need in relation to services for older people (which might usefully inform service development).

1.11 An independent researcher conducted an evaluation of the training and the implementation of the pilot projects. The draft policies, procedures and guidelines were amended in light of these findings. A copy of the Evaluation Brief is contained in Appendix C. A summary of the Evaluation is published separately.

CHAPTER 2

Recommendations

Introduction

2.1 We recommend that **the response to elder abuse be placed in the wider context of health and social care services for older people.**

2.2 At present, however, the absence of a satisfactory framework for service provision for older people prevents the development of a standardised approach. There are currently significant gaps in the provision of services in both community and extended care, including a lack of services on a twenty-four-hour, seven-days-a-week basis; a lack of social work services for older people; and inadequate support services for carers. (Garavan, McGee and Winder, 2001) Services are unevenly distributed and this gives rise to anomalies in terms of equity of access to services for older people. There is the absence of national standards of care and a lack of regulations governing statutory residential care for older people. An observation made by a clinician during the evaluation of the pilot projects highlights the effects of such gaps:

> "Elder abuse is something that happens culturally and corporately as well as on an individual basis . . . a lot of the abuse that goes on is purely unintentional abuse that is institutionalised. It comes from the structures of health and social care that we have in place at the moment . . . some people are being looked after in impoverished environments . . . being treated and cared for by over-worked, stressed, burnt-out staff who are too small in number to be able to cater for their needs properly . . . the wider definition of what abuse is needs to be highlighted very quickly and emphatically as well".

We therefore strongly recommend that **existing Government policy — The Years Ahead**, (as updated by *The Years Ahead — A Review of Implementation of its Recommendations*) and *Quality and Fairness* (which includes *An Action Plan for Dementia*) — **be urgently and fully implemented**. In addition, we agree with the NCAOP that **urgent attention** should be given to the **provision of a formal framework to ensure quality of care for older people living in both community and institutional settings**.

We have found that previous work on child abuse in the Irish setting has shaped health and social care professionals' perceptions, expectations and anxieties about responding to elder abuse. Learning from this work supports our recommendation that **a holistic approach, with integrated services and staff equipped with the skills and knowledge to respond to both the protection and wider health and social care needs of older people,** is indeed the best approach.

We recognise that a key challenge for staff is to meet the welfare, safety and support needs of older people suffering from or at risk of abuse and to initiate processes that will contribute to their well-being in the long term. The **procedures** we recommend are intended to **maximise the sense of confidence, trust and safety with which staff can do this.** They are practical and adaptable rather than aspirational.

Policy

2.3   We recommend that a **clear policy on elder abuse is formulated and implemented at all levels of governance within the health, social and protection services in Ireland.** This encompasses public (statutory), private and voluntary services. The **policy we recommend** supports a holistic approach and emphasises **three main goals: an appropriate staff structure; good practice;** and **appropriate** and **ongoing training for all those working with older people**.

2.4   The lead provider of health and social care services for older people in Ireland are the ten health boards and those contracted to provide services to them. **We recommend that each health board develop a strategy to implement the policy recommendations made in this report.** The policy, and any initiatives related to it, must be integrated into the wider policy and framework of health and social care services for older people.

2.5   The aim of the **policy**, and the procedures that flow from it, is to promote and sustain a multi-disciplinary, holistic approach to elder abuse, with collaboration between all those providing health and social care to older people. We recommend that it should therefore be **developed in consultation with health board legal departments, Gardaí, local authorities and other public, private and voluntary organisations, and, where possible, with representatives of older people**.

Staff structure

2.6   We recommend that, <u>**at a minimum**</u> the following **staff structure** be put in place:

- A **Steering Group** in each health board area

- A half-time **Dedicated Health Board Officer** with responsibility for Elder Abuse in each community care area

- **A Senior Case-Worker** for each community care area, employed by the health board

- **Secretarial support.**

2.7   **The Steering Group** should comprise **representatives from the public sector** (that is, An Garda Síochána, local authorities, the Department of Social and Family Affairs, and the health boards themselves), representatives from **private and voluntary sector organisations,** and from **representative groups for older people**. We recommend that the **main task of the Steering Group** (in conjunction with the Dedicated Officer and the Senior Case-Worker) **will be to develop and implement a framework for action on elder abuse,** including the mechanisms for establishing and overseeing the services needed to respond to elder abuse.

2.8   Each health board, through this mechanism, should ensure that **clear pathways are identified for dealing with allegations of elder abuse,** including those that occur outside normal working hours. Further details of the membership of the Steering Group and its roles and responsibilities, the Dedicated Officer and the Senior Case-Worker are given in Chapter 5.

2.9   We recommend that a **dedicated budget in the region of €4.25 million per annum be set aside for the provision of staff and services, as well as for a National Centre** to provide a focus for national research and support for training. A detailed breakdown of this figure is given in Chapter 7. This minimum allocation should be reviewed formally by 2007, at the latest, to determine whether or not it is large enough to provide the resources needed for responding to elder abuse.

Legislation

2.10   We recommend **legislation to establish older people's entitlement to core community care services** following assessment of need, including home help or home care, therapist services, day care, meals service and respite care.

2.11   **Legislation** is needed **to provide for Garda access** in situations where there is a concern that elder abuse is taking place but **where access is not available in order to get consent**. Current legal provisions do not include access in these situations. This legislation should give power to An Garda Síochána, where there are reasonable grounds to suspect that elder abuse has taken place, to enter on any premises, if needs be by force, to gain access to the older person in order to interview them. Such an interview would be in order to establish if they wish to consent, or are in a position or able to give consent, to further investigation and intervention for their protection and welfare. This provision should stipulate that for the purposes of such interview and/or assessment the Gardaí may be accompanied by health and social personnel as appropriate. We also recommend that the access provision in any new Act be reviewed in five years time to evaluate its effectiveness.

2.12   A key concern is the need for legal support to secure the protection of vulnerable older people who cannot protect themselves from harm and abuse, be it because of mental incapacity or the consequences of extreme abuse. We are therefore recommending that **changes be made to the Ward of Court System, the Lunacy Regulations (Ireland) Act 1870 and the Enduring Power of Attorney system.** We also recommend the introduction of appropriate mental health legislation.

     a.   **The Ward of Court System** generally provides protection for older people with impaired capacity who have not made provision for enduring power of attorney. We support the Law Reform Commission in seeking a radical change in the Ward of Court System. We consider that this should include the introduction of a Public Guardian, as proposed by the Law Reform Commission. This service should include:

         •   Means to provide for <u>both</u> the welfare and financial decisions of the older person with impaired capacity

         •   Up to date, appropriate language

         •   Provisions for fast track proceedings where an emergency exists

- Appropriate resources to ensure the protection of an older person at risk in emergencies

- Appropriate supervisory arrangements

- Measures to protect older people with temporary impaired capacity.

b. We recommend that the **Enduring Power of Attorney (EPA) system be re-evaluated**. Namely that:

- Adequate supervision and review be put in place for the EPA in the management of the older person's finances and welfare to prevent possible abuse.

- Awareness campaigns be conducted among health, legal and social care professionals on the benefits of EPA for their clients.

- Measures against abuse be built into the system.

2.13   The current **Mental Health Act 2001** contains provisions governing the involuntary admission of patients. It does not, however, include measures for the protection of people with impaired capacity at risk from abuse. We recommend the **introduction and full implementation of the Adult Care Order proposed in the White Paper on Mental Health 1998.** This allows for the removal to a place of safety of a person with impaired capacity who is at risk of abuse. The proposed Adult Care Order stipulates that a Consultant Psychiatrist is responsible for the medical diagnosis of impaired capacity. We believe this process should be initiated by a Medical Practitioner who is familiar to the older person.

2.14   We recommend that future **mental health legislation** should include provision to protect from an abusive situation those older people **with temporary impaired capacity**, such as delirium.

2.15   **Legislation** is needed as a matter of urgency **to protect both the public and health and social care workers who report elder abuse** in good faith from any negative consequences that might arise from their allegation. This may take the form of provisions in the Protection of Persons Reporting Child Abuse Act 1998.

2.16   We recommend the **extension of the Social Service Inspectorate** to all community and residential services to older people, as recommended in the Health Strategy (2001).

Impaired Capacity

2.17   In the light of the under development of services for people with dementia and their carers — both very vulnerable groups in the context of elder abuse — **we recommend the urgent implementation of An Action Plan for Dementia** (as recommended in *Quality and Fairness*) to ensure early diagnosis, adequate care structures and early implementation of good practice, such as the Enduring Power of Attorney system.

Carers

2.18   We also recommend that **adequate support and provision of services be made available to all carers, not only carers of those with dementia**. Caring for dependent people can be a source of major strain and psychological and emotional distress (O'Shea, 2000). Adequate support and access to appropriate services for carers can help prevent elder abuse.

Awareness, education and training

2.19   We recommend that a **public awareness programme,** under the direction of the Department of Health and Children, be undertaken to raise awareness of elder abuse among the general public in Ireland. In addition, so that all relevant service-providers are aware of the steps being taken to respond to elder abuse, we recommend that the introduction of the policy and procedures be accompanied by a **nationwide publicity and promotion campaign aimed at those involved in the health and social care of older people.**

2.20   We recommend that senior staff in health boards and service-providers, including those in the voluntary and private sectors, undergo **induction and training before the implementation of policy and procedures.** Training of all other staff should follow. Training should be designed to meet the needs of specific groups of staff.

2.21   In addition, we recommend that the **curricula of professional training courses and Continuing Professional Development education for health and social care workers and those in legal and financial services be expanded to include elder abuse.** This is particularly important for those groups involved in primary care (for example, General Practitioners and Public Health Nurses); there is considerable evidence to show that identification of elder abuse by the primary care team is critical in reducing the incidence of abuse.

Financial abuse

2.22   Financial abuse is a widespread concern. Like many other forms of abuse, it is difficult to identify; in particular, it is difficult to distinguish between acceptable exchange and exploitative conduct, between misconduct and mismanagement. To tackle this, we recommend that **national and regional education and awareness programmes be developed.** These should be targeted at two main groups: older people and the general public — to create awareness of the risks and consequences of financial abuse and to encourage older people to seek independent legal advice when making major decisions; and health and social care workers and legal and financial professionals — to develop the skills needed to recognise, address and minimise financial abuse against older people. These **programmes should be developed** by the Irish Bankers' Federation (IBF), the Department of Social and Family Affairs, An Garda Síochána, the health boards and older people's organisations, in association with the **National Implementation Group** (discussed in section 2.26) overseeing the implementation of the Working Group's recommendations.

2.23   We also recommend that the Department of Social and Family Affairs compiles and **implements financial planning schemes** for 'at risk' older people through the Money Advice Bureaux.

2.24   In addition, we recommend that the IBF and its members set up a system that gives banks **permission to contact a named person(s) (or the Public Guardian) if there is suspicion of financial abuse on an older person's account.**

Advocacy

2.25   The Department of Social and Family Affairs should facilitate access to an **advocacy service** for older people in long-term residential care so as to enable them to protect their financial and/or property assets and to have their opinions heard and their wishes respected when making decisions and transactions.

Implementation

2.26   We recommend that the **Department of Health and Children immediately establish a National Implementation Group** to guide the implementation of the recommendations outlined in this report and to ensure that they are fully in place by mid-2005.

Research and education

2.27   In addition to this implementation body, there is a need for the provision of the following education and research services to facilitate the implementation process. This is important both in terms of maintaining and developing the considerable 'community of knowledge' relating to elder abuse which has been fostered and developed by the Working Group, and also because of the dearth of primary research on elder abuse in Ireland. The services needed include:

- a service to provide information, advice and support on elder abuse to service-planners and providers of services to older people

- a service to provide induction and ongoing training on elder abuse and

- substantive original research on elder abuse in Ireland.

We recommend that the Department of Health and Children **National Implementation Group immediately establish and fund a National Centre** which combines both practitioner and academic knowledge relevant to elder abuse to meet educational needs, as well as developing a programme of research to support and underpin policy and best practice and service provision. Topics should include:

- Training and education.

- Older people's perceptions of elder abuse.

- Public perception of ageing/older people.

- Development of approaches to elder abuse which focus on empowerment of vulnerable older people.

- The need for structured counselling services for those suffering from elder abuse.

- Development of strategic approaches to the prevention, identification and management of elder abuse in institutional settings.

- Identifying current practices in residential care that result in the abuse of older people.

- Evaluation of the results of elder abuse interventions.

Reporting abuse

2.28 If these recommendations are implemented, we recommend **that mandatory reporting of elder abuse should not be considered at this time**. There is no persuasive evidence that it leads to successful outcomes for older people suffering abuse; indeed, it may prevent people seeking help because of the legal and cultural ramifications it has for both the person suffering the abuse and also for the perpetrator.

Review

2.29 We recommend that a formal national review of a) policy and procedures on elder abuse and their implementation and b) the legislative changes, be carried out in 2007.

CHAPTER 3

Definition of Elder Abuse

Introduction

3.1 Elder abuse is complex and difficult to define precisely. No one definition is universally accepted as encompassing all aspects of abuse that need to be considered. For instance, some definitions are thought to focus on abuse in the home or within the family, to the exclusion or underestimation of abuse in residential care, or to the exclusion of societal abuse, a form of abuse which deprives older people of basic services.

3.2 Settling on a definition, however, is important to the process of taking action. On the one hand, it is important to think of elder abuse as an umbrella term for the wide range of harm that can affect older people — defining it too narrowly risks constraining the development of an appropriate response to it. On the other hand, it is necessary at this stage in the development of a response to the issue in Ireland to provide a more precise definition, in order to facilitate co-ordinated action.

Definition

3.3 We therefore recommend that elder abuse be defined as:

"A single or repeated act or lack of appropriate action occurring within any relationship where there is an expectation of trust which causes harm or distress to an older person or violates their human and civil rights."

This definition is based on that used by the United Kingdom organisation, Action on Elder Abuse.

3.4 It is important to note that this definition excludes self-neglect and abuse by strangers since these were not in our terms of reference. In common with other countries, we take 65 years of age as the point beyond which abuse may be considered to be elder abuse.

3.5 Although this definition focuses on acts of abuse by individuals, we recognise that abuse also arises from inadequacy of care (as a result of a lack of resources). We hope that the good practice guidance given here will help to overcome this aspect of the problem.

3.6 We recommend that the definition is reviewed as knowledge of elder abuse and experience in dealing with it develops.

3.7   There are several forms of abuse, any or all of which may be perpetrated as the result of deliberate intent, negligence or ignorance (indicators of elder abuse can be found in Appendix D):

- *Physical abuse*, including hitting, slapping, pushing, kicking, misuse of medication, restraint, or inappropriate sanctions.

- *Sexual abuse*, including rape and sexual assault or sexual acts to which the older adult has not consented, or could not consent, or into which he or she was compelled to consent.

- *Psychological abuse*, including emotional abuse, threats of harm or abandonment, deprivation of contact, humiliation, blaming, controlling, intimidation, coercion, harassment, verbal abuse, isolation or withdrawal from services or supportive networks.

- *Financial or material abuse,* including theft, fraud, exploitation, pressure in connection with wills, property or inheritance or financial transactions, or the misuse or misappropriation of property, possessions or benefits.

- *Neglect and acts of omission,* including ignoring medical or physical care needs, failure to provide access to appropriate health, social care or educational services, the withholding of the necessities of life, such as medication, adequate nutrition and heating.

- *Discriminatory abuse,* including racism, sexism that based on a person's disability, and other forms of harassment, slurs or similar treatment.

When abuse is a criminal offence

3.8   Some instances of abuse constitute a criminal offence. In this respect, older adults are entitled to the protection of the law in the same way as any other member of the public. Examples of actions that might constitute criminal offences are physical assault, sexual assault and rape, theft and fraud or other forms of financial exploitation.

The circumstances

3.9   Abuse can take place in any context. It may occur when an older person lives alone or with a relative; it may occur within residential or day-care settings, in hospitals, home support services and other places assumed to be safe, or in public places.

The abuser

3.10   A wide range of people may abuse older people, including relatives and family members, professional staff, paid care workers, volunteers, other service users, neighbours, friends and associates.

Patterns of abuse and abusing

3.11   Patterns of abuse and abusing vary and reflect different circumstances:

- *Long-term abuse,* in the context of an ongoing family relationship, such as domestic violence or sexual abuse between spouses or generations.

- *Opportunistic abuse,* such as theft occurring because money has been left around.

- **Situational abuse,** which arises because pressures have built up and/or because of the difficult or challenging behaviour of the older person.

- **Neglect of a person's needs** because those around him or her are not able to be responsible for their care; for example if the carer has difficulties because of debt, alcohol or mental health problems.

- **Institutional abuse,** which may comprise of poor care standards, lack of positive responses to complex needs, rigid routines, inadequate staffing, and an insufficient knowledge base within the service.

- **Unacceptable 'treatments' or 'programmes',** which include sanctions or punishment, such as the withholding of food and drink, seclusion, the unnecessary and unauthorised use of control and restraint, or the over- or under-medication.

- **Racist and discriminatory practice** by staff, including ageism, racism and other discriminatory practices, which may be attributable to the lack of appropriate guidance.

- **Inability to get access to key services** such as health care, dentistry, prostheses.

- **Misappropriation of benefits and/or use of the person's money** by other members of the household or by care staff.

- **Fraud or intimidation** in connection with wills, property or other assets.

3.12 The seriousness or extent of abuse is often not clear when concern about it is first expressed. It is important, therefore, when considering the appropriateness of intervention, to approach reports of incidents or allegations with an open mind. In making any assessment of seriousness, the following factors should be considered:

- the vulnerability of the individual

- the nature and extent of the abuse

- the length of time it has been occurring

- the impact on the individual

- the risk of repeated or increasingly serious acts involving this person or other older people.

CHAPTER 4

Policy

Policy content

4.1   We recommend that each health board develop a policy that clearly sets out its responsibilities to:

- Develop an integrated service in relation to elder abuse, taking into account the wide variety of health, social and protection agencies that need to be part of that service.

- Place elder abuse in the wider context of older people's right to and need for health and social care.

- Provide care in the most appropriate setting and promote best practice in all care settings to help prevent elder abuse.

- Recognise that a significant number of older Irish people are subject to elder abuse in various forms.

- Ask staff and contracted service-providers to report their concerns about suspected abuse.

- Acknowledge the challenges that staff face in addressing the issue of elder abuse.

- Associate the reporting of elder abuse with the concept of 'duty of care' to the vulnerable people in their care.

- Provide the resources and the mechanisms to identify and assess elder abuse, to make appropriate interventions and, where possible, to prevent it.

- Identify mechanisms for monitoring and reviewing the implementation and the impact of policy.

- Provide support, including legal advice, to all staff, including the Dedicated Officer, the Senior Case-Worker and the Steering Group, in the conduct of their duties.

4.2   Health boards have, or are in the process of developing, strategies and policy to provide for the health and social care needs of older people, in response to the National Health Strategy (2001) and the Primary Care Strategy (2001) and to a number of reports from the NCAOP.[1] We recommend that policy on elder abuse be integrated into this policy

---

[1] These include Framework for Quality in Long-Term Residential Care for Older People in Ireland (2000); An Action Plan for Dementia (1999); The Costs of Caring for People with Dementia and Related Cognitive Impairments (2000); Care and Case Management for Older People in Ireland (2001); and Health and Social Services for Older People (HeSSOP, 2001).

framework. Other agencies, either statutory or non-statutory, should develop parallel policies covering their fields of responsibility or involvement.

Underlying principles

4.3   In developing and implementing policy, and any procedures flowing from it, the health board should:

- *Actively encourage the empowerment and well-being* of older adults through the services they provide.

- Act in a way that supports *the rights of the individual* to lead an independent life based on self-determination and personal choice.

- *Recognise people who are unable* to make their own decisions and/or to protect themselves, their assets and their bodily integrity, and ensure adequate protection for them.

- Recognise that the *right to self-determination* can involve risk and ensure that such risk is recognised and understood by all concerned and is minimised whenever possible.

- Although intervention may, in some cases, compromise the individual older person's right to independence and choice, *the principle of 'least restrictive alternative'* should apply at all times.

- Ensure that the law and statutory requirements are known and used appropriately so that *older people receive the protection of the law and access to the judicial process.*

4.4   We recognise that in practice adherence to these principles may pose challenges — for example, in resolving issues of autonomy and risk to the individual — and may highlight the need for further development of services for older people.

4.5   All organisations involved in providing health and social care to older people must also have a policy on internal and external whistleblowing or 'disclosure in the public interest' within the wider framework of a risk management policy. This should make clear that both internal and external whistleblowing are acceptable to the organisation and that victimisation of those who make reports will not be tolerated.

4.6   Organisations should have a written policy on confidentiality. Services and agencies should draw up a common agreement on confidentiality which sets out the principles governing the sharing of information based on the best interests of the older person. This should make clear the distinction between safeguarding the best interests of the service-user and protecting other aspects of management.

Implementing the policy

4.7   Implementing an elder abuse policy, and setting up the necessary structure to support it, presents a significant challenge. To ensure that the process runs smoothly, and that service operations are comprehensive and effective, we recommend that each health board prepares an implementation strategy. The strategy should cover the following activities (some of which may run in parallel):

Development of staff and management structure

- Establishment of the Steering Group.

- Clarification of roles and responsibilities, authority and accountability of the individual health board and other service-providers.

- Recruitment of key staff.

Development of a feedback system

- Development of a system for monitoring referrals, the outcome of cases and the impact of interventions, and the implications of all this in terms of service development (including unmet need) and resources.

- Development of a system for incorporating this knowledge into training programmes and into the ongoing development of policy and procedures at local and national level.

Development and introduction of service procedures

- Development of policy, procedures and guidelines for responding to concerns and referrals, including the design of reporting arrangements, appropriate to the health board setting.

Awareness-raising and training

- Development and time-tabling of awareness-raising programmes to ensure that all staff and all service users are aware of health board policy, understand what abuse is and know how to report concerns.

- Development and time-tabling of a comprehensive training plan, including induction training, for all staff at every level on policy, procedures and professional practice, in line with their needs and commensurate with their responsibilities.

CHAPTER 5

Staff Structure

Introduction

5.1 It is important that initiatives on elder abuse are embedded or 'mainstreamed' within health and social care services for older people. Their success will depend on effective collaboration among all organisations providing care to older people and among staff from all disciplines and at all levels. Effective collaboration will in turn depend on the existence of a suitable structure at health board level and clearly defined operating procedures. We describe the structure below; guidance for developing procedures is given in the next chapter.

Staff structure

5.2 The structure we recommend will comprise a Steering Group, a Dedicated Officer with responsibility for Elder Abuse, a Senior Case-Worker and adequate secretarial support.

5.3 We recommend that, as a minimum, one Steering Group be established in each health board area. In each community care area we recommend, as a minimum, one half-time Dedicated Officer (although experience from the pilot programme suggests the value of full-time involvement during the start-up/implementation phase) and one full-time Senior Case-Worker.

5.4 We envisage that the person holding the post of Dedicated Officer will have other duties involving the health and social care of older people. We believe that this link with other parts of the service will facilitate the integration of the elder abuse service.

5.5 It will be the responsibility of this team — the Steering Group, the Dedicated Officer and the Senior Case-Worker — on behalf of the health board to:

- Devise and oversee the policy on elder abuse.

- Create awareness of elder abuse among all health and social care staff.

- Promote the training of all health and social care staff dealing with older people.

- Guide the development of policy and best practice for the prevention of elder abuse.

- Develop procedures and guidelines appropriate for responding to elder abuse in both community and institutional settings.

- Ensure that agencies contracted to provide services to the health board have policy, procedures and guidelines on elder abuse which are consistent with those of the health board.

- Facilitate effective working relationships between health boards and other agencies that deliver services to older people.

- Liaise with other agencies, including An Garda Síochána, in the event of a criminal investigation.

The Steering Group

5.6   While we recommend a common response to elder abuse throughout the State, we recognise that there are, and will continue to be, differences in service provision and delivery among health boards and that these differences may mean differences in approach at health board level. Therefore, the primary role of the Steering Group will be to develop, plan, co-ordinate, support, monitor and evaluate an approach suitable to that particular health board setting. This role will include reviewing and updating procedures on an ongoing basis.

Membership

5.7   The Steering Group should bring together representatives of service providers to older people. It should include those with more specialised perspectives as required (see Appendix E).

Responsibilities

5.8   The Steering Group will be responsible on behalf of the health board for:

- ***Identifying roles, responsibilities, authority and accountability*** with regard to the action each service and professional group should take to ensure the welfare and protection of older people.

- ***Establishing mechanisms for implementing*** policies and strategies for protecting older people.

- ***Applying procedures and guidelines*** in the context of existing services and advising on the need for the development of other services.

- ***Indicating the pathway within the health board for responding to elder abuse***, and dealing with complaints, grievances and professional and administrative malpractice.

- ***Supporting the Dedicated Officer who has responsibility for Elder Abuse***.

5.9   More specifically, its role will be to:

- Contribute to the creation of a shared knowledge base about elder abuse in the local setting, both through the exchange of information and experience from different disciplines and work settings, and via input from guest participants.

- Enable a network of support to be created for staff and their actions.

- Identify issues that may need to be examined within the elder abuse response framework and participate in the formulation of resolutions of those issues.

- Facilitate discussion of and provide advice and guidance to staff on strategic issues arising during the response to a case.

- Advise on the suitability of procedures and guidelines for work settings.

- Create links between departments, services and agencies involved in providing care to older people.

5.10   The role of each Steering Group member will be to:

- Disseminate information from the Steering Group to colleagues in his or her discipline or work setting.

- Enable access to and participation of his or her staff in awareness-raising and training.

- Promote the reporting of elder abuse concerns from his or her work setting.

- Identify barriers and opportunities in relation to the reporting and subsequent action on elder abuse in his or her work setting and bring both to the attention of the Steering Group.

- Act as a resource on the basis of his or her experience and expertise to the Steering Group and to staff involved with elder abuse.

Dedicated Health Board Officer with responsibility for Elder Abuse

5.11   The Dedicated Officer (his or her precise title to be decided by each health board) will be a position at senior managerial level in the health board with experience in service delivery to older people. He or she will be supported in this role by the Steering Group. He or she will have line management responsibility, for operational purposes, for the Senior Case-Worker.

Responsibilities

5.12   He or she will have responsibility for the development, implementation and evaluation of the health board's response to elder abuse. The post should therefore be at a level that gives the post-holder the authority to carry out this responsibility. In addition, he or she will be responsible for identifying and liaising with those inside the health board and with those outside agencies that have responsibility for the welfare and protection of older people in the health board area, in order to promote the policies and procedures on elder abuse.

5.13   Further, the Dedicated Officer, alone or in collaboration with the Senior Case-Worker (and others in the health board), may be responsible for developing and organising training sessions and workshops to disseminate, throughout the organisation, the knowledge gained in dealing with referrals and assessing and managing cases of elder abuse.

Core attributes

5.14   Core attributes suitable for undertaking the role are:

- Commitment to client-centred service provision

- Commitment to the interests of older people

- Management experience

- In-depth knowledge of services and personnel within the health board setting

- Professional experience in order to support the Case-Worker in his or her duties and arranging appropriate professional supervision for him or her.

The Senior Case-Worker

5.15   The Senior Case-Worker will report to the Dedicated Officer.

Responsibilities

5.16   He or she will be responsible, in conjunction with appropriate service-providers within the health board, for the assessment of cases of suspected elder abuse referred to the health board. The responsibilities of the role will also include day-to-day management and investigation of allegations and complaints of elder abuse and/or awareness and prevention programmes. He or she will have responsibility for liaising with the Nursing Home Inspection Team in its investigation of complaints under Section 23 and 26 of the Nursing Home (Care and Welfare) Regulations 1993. He or she will also be responsible for implementing Section 6 of The Domestic Violence Act 1996.

Core attributes

5.17   Social work training provides the core competencies required for the Senior Case-Worker role, but other professions may have or may acquire them through training. They include:

- Interviewing and communication skills, including the ability to establish rapport and develop relationships with older people and their families.

- Assessment, negotiation and consultation skills.

- Case management skills.

5.18   In addition, it is important that the person recruited has a commitment to both client-centred service provision and the interests of older people. It will also be essential for the Senior Case-Worker to have/acquire knowledge of the relevant law and a familiarity with mental health services and mental health issues.

Integrating the service

5.19   In order to integrate the elder abuse response within the wider framework of services for older people, it may be advisable to locate the Senior Case-Worker within or alongside the multi-disciplinary health and social care teams. Placing the service in this context also supports the care management approach outlined in the National Health Strategy (2001).

5.20   We acknowledge that this integration may be difficult to achieve, and may continue to be so, given probable future changes, including the development of primary care teams.

5.21   We stress that it is essential that the health board team takes responsibility for developing channels of communication and liaising with those other agencies that may be involved in the process of reporting, assessing, investigating or otherwise dealing with allegations or cases of the abuse of older people.

5.22 It will be necessary to plan for, negotiate and, if necessary, resource multi-disciplinary participation into the elder abuse assessment and management process. We recognise, however, that with heavy workloads, this may not always be easy or possible. In the pilot projects, for example, Geriatricians and General Practitioners found it difficult to set aside the time needed. It may be necessary to find other ways of supporting their participation — for example, by providing extra staff or remuneration for time involved.

Expertise

5.23 In the ongoing management of cases, health board staff should consult internal sources for advice and guidance and, where appropriate external sources. Some useful sources of information and advice are provided in Appendix F.

CHAPTER 6

Procedures

Introduction

6.1   The aim of this chapter is to guide in the development of procedures, those responsible for policy on elder abuse in public, private and voluntary organisations and, in particular, those working in health boards. We outline what matters these procedures must cover and we offer guidance on content, stating where appropriate, the underlying principles.

6.2   An organisation's employees, its agents, its contractors and its service-users must be able to identify elder abuse, report their concerns about it and be reassured that raising concerns is important.

6.3   Identification of elder abuse, however, is complex and difficult. Those suffering abuse are often isolated from social networks and from contact with professionals. The deliberate action of the abuser may make access difficult. The belief that family privacy is paramount can be a barrier to intervention. Identification may be hindered by denial: the older person may be reluctant to admit that he or she has been or is being abused to avoid embarrassment or shame, or for fear of abandonment, reprisal or institutionalisation. A carer may be reluctant to admit abuse for obvious reasons.

6.4   The development of a policy on elder abuse will help with identification by raising awareness of the problem and sensitising to it, those who provide services to older people. Training and education should serve to increase awareness and sensitivity. Training should also aim to develop the skills necessary for identification: the ability to gather information in a sensitive way, to understand the older person's thoughts and feelings about the situation and to build a trusting relationship. These skills are crucial to the success of any initiative: practitioners report that identification (and intervention) is a process rather than a one-off event and depends to a great extent on establishing a trusting relationship.

6.5   The role of procedures — instructions to staff that inform them of the action to take in responding to cases of alleged elder abuse — is to further the aims of policy and training. The use of procedures should ensure that there is a consistent response to reports of elder abuse and to the handling of cases: procedures should be designed in a way that enables assessments and investigations to be handled sensitively, appropriately and with confidence.

6.6   We realise that there will be a great deal of variation in both the settings and the circumstances in which these procedures will be used. For example, different types of abuse will present different dilemmas; different health boards and different settings (community and residential care) will have different structures and practices within which procedures will operate. The procedures we outline here should therefore be used as a basic framework, the starting point from which to develop procedures suitable to particular settings and circumstances.

What procedures must cover

6.7 Procedures should be developed that include:

(a) A statement of specific roles and responsibilities, authority and accountability (to ensure that all staff understand their role and their limitations).

(b) A statement of the procedures for dealing with allegations of abuse, including those for dealing with emergencies.

(c) Contact details of those to whom an allegation should be referred, inside and outside normal working hours.

(d) Details of inter-service communication channels and procedures for decision-making.

(e) A statement indicating what to do in the event of a failure to take necessary action.

(f) A list of sources of expert advice.

(g) A list of services that might offer advice and support to older people.

6.8 These procedures should not be set in stone but should be evaluated and updated regularly to incorporate learning from practice.

Key content in detail

Dealing with complaints or allegations

6.9 Information may come from a variety of sources including the older person suffering abuse, a concerned relative, or a health and social care worker. The information may come in the form of a complaint or an expression of concern, or it may come to light during a health or social care assessment.

6.10 It is worth noting that, in the first instance, this information may not come with the knowledge or consent of the older person who is suffering the abuse. Therefore, further evaluation should take place with his or her knowledge and consent, if he or she has capacity and is free from undue duress.

6.11 The process of responding to cases of elder abuse — from identification to intervention — will take some time and will depend on the development of a relationship of trust.

Reporting

6.12 We recommend that formal reporting procedures be developed for use within organisations and for communicating reports of alleged elder abuse to other appropriate agencies, as required. This does not and should not prevent informal discussion with the Senior Case-Worker, for example, to determine whether abuse has taken place, to get advice on carrying out further assessment or investigation and so on. In fact, this should be encouraged, because it will help to educate health and social service workers about what is an appropriate (formal) referral.

6.13 We recognise that formal reporting procedures may, in the short term, hinder the emergence of elder abuse concerns. Experience shows, however, that as staff become familiar with and gain confidence in the policy and procedures (and in their own ability to respond), anxiety about formal reporting diminishes and acceptance of it as part of professional responsibility and duty of care grows.

Basic reporting procedure

6.14 <u>All</u> reports and/or suspicions of abuse should be taken seriously. Any health and social care or protection worker who receives information, suspects or is concerned that an older person has been abused, is being abused or is at risk of abuse should discuss the matter with his or her line manager as soon as possible. A written referral form should be completed at the earliest opportunity following this discussion and sent to the health board-appointed Senior Case-Worker, who will take responsibility for it and begin an assessment or investigation. In some circumstances the suspicion or allegation may be reported directly to the Senior Case-Worker, while at the same time informing a line manager that this step is being taken.

6.15 This basic reporting procedure applies to health and social care workers in all settings. Those working in non-health board services and agencies, including those in the voluntary and private sector, should assess reports or complaints of elder abuse locally in the first instance, as they would any other type of complaint. If an initial assessment suggests that abuse has, is or is likely to be taking place, then an informal discussion or a formal referral to the Senior Case-Worker, whichever is appropriate to the circumstances, is in order.

Basic Reporting Procedure

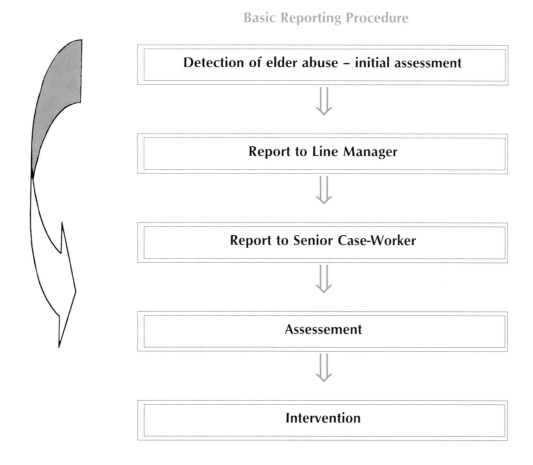

Detection of elder abuse – initial assessment

⇓

Report to Line Manager

⇓

Report to Senior Case-Worker

⇓

Assessement

⇓

Intervention

6.16   This reporting procedure should be designed to reflect existing work practices and the range of settings and sources from which referrals will come (including members of the public). For example, Home Helps or General Nurses working in the community may consult Public Health Nurses, who may take the matter further within their own system; Staff Nurses may consult with Ward Sisters before reporting a concern.

Assurances to those making a complaint

6.17   All those making a complaint, whether staff, service-users, carers or members of the general public, should be assured of the following:

- Their remarks will be taken seriously.

- Their comments will be treated in confidence but their concerns may be shared if they or others are at significant risk.

- They will be dealt with in a fair and equitable manner.

- They will be kept informed of action that has been taken and its outcome within a reasonable time limit.

- If they are service-users, they will be given immediate protection, where possible, from the risk of reprisals or intimidation.

- If they are service-providers, they will be given support and afforded protection.

Dealing with anonymous reports and complaints

6.18   Concerns reported anonymously should be followed up, depending on the content of the report and the nature of any other information about the older person held by the service-provider.

6.19   Those reporting anonymously should be informed that anonymity may restrict the ability of professionals to access information or to intervene to protect the older person. The anonymous reporter should be urged to identify himself or herself and encouraged to make a statement in writing or in person.

6.20   If an anonymous report is made through a third party, the person mediating should be asked to facilitate contact between the person reporting and the health board.

Procedures for reporting concerns about abuse by employees

6.21   Each organisation should provide written guidance on reporting concerns about suspected abuse by employees. It should state clearly what action will be taken if allegations of abuse are made against an employee. There should be clear procedures indicating what the person reporting the concern should do if they feel that inappropriate or insufficient action has been taken. The organisation should make clear to employees, to which external organisation they should report in situations where they feel they cannot report internally or where they are dissatisfied with the internal response.

Record-keeping

6.22 When a complaint or allegation of abuse is received, a clear and accurate record of it and any action taken in relation to it must be made. All relevant details should be incorporated into the service and the service-user's file.

6.23 Files may be used in legal and/or disciplinary proceedings; in addition, under the Freedom of Information Act 1997, people have a right to see what is written about them in health board and other files. Staff, via training and written guidance, should be instructed about how to record information, what information is relevant and what information should not be recorded for fear that it may be in breach of a person's legal rights. The issue of confidentiality of information should also be examined.

Responding in individual cases

6.24 An investigation will consist of the following stages:

- Reporting to a single referral point (that is, the health board Senior Case-Worker).

- Recording (with sensitivity to the suspected abused person and to the alleged perpetrator) the precise factual details of the alleged abuse.

- Liaising with those in other services (e.g. via a strategy meeting) that may have a role in a subsequent investigation.

- Investigating/assessing the case within an agreed framework (this is the role of the Senior Case-Worker).

- Making a decision.

6.25 The Senior Case-Worker, in conjunction with relevant staff, will co-ordinate and conduct the assessment of the allegation of abuse.

6.26 The objectives of the assessment or investigation should be to:

- Establish the facts.

- Assess the need of the older person for protection, support and redress.

- Make decisions about what action should be taken in relation to the perpetrator, the service or its management, if they have been culpable, ineffective or negligent.

Management and co-ordination of the response to allegations

6.27 The task of investigating an allegation or complaint will involve the management and co-ordination of the following, several of which may run in parallel:

- Investigation of the complaint.

- Assessment of needs and care planning for the person at the centre of the allegation.

- Action to determine if a crime has occurred.

- Action by employers (e.g. suspension, disciplinary proceedings, development of and use of complaints and grievance procedures, action to remove the perpetrator from the professional register).

- Arrangements for treatment or care of the suspected perpetrator, if appropriate.

- Consideration of the implications relating to regulation, inspection and contract monitoring.

6.28 An investigation should be co-ordinated in a way that ensures that there is no unnecessary duplication, especially in interviewing the older person or the alleged perpetrator of the abuse.

6.29 There may be a joint investigation (for example between An Garda Síochána and the health board, or the health board and a non-health board service) but any shared information must be constantly evaluated and reviewed by each service.

6.30 The health board through the Senior-Case Worker will co-ordinate and monitor the investigation and any action taken and should ensure that the Dedicated Officer and any other services involved receive updates on the progress of the investigation, unless it is unsafe for them to do so. The roles of the Dedicated Officer, the Steering Group and the Senior Case-Worker include facilitating this inter-service co-operation.

Garda involvement

6.31 In exceptional circumstances, especially if the matter is very serious or there is evidence that a criminal offence has taken place, the first notification might be to the Gardaí. Health boards and An Garda Síochána should establish a framework, which will include agreed protocols and procedures on elder abuse. In such cases the Gardaí may seek the following:

(a) to be afforded the opportunity to interview the subject first and alone

(b) that interviewing of subjects is kept to a minimum until the matter is resolved, so that the defence cannot allege that the evidence is rehearsed; and

(c) that any witnesses are not allowed to discuss the matter with the accused or with other witnesses.

6.32 An early referral to or consultation with the Gardaí, however, does not mean that criminal proceedings will follow, and it may have benefits:

- It may enable the Gardaí to establish whether or not a criminal act has been committed and so allow them to determine if, and at what stage, they need to become involved.

- A higher standard of proof is required in criminal proceedings than in disciplinary or regulatory proceedings, and early involvement can help the Gardaí to ensure that forensic evidence is not lost or contaminated.

- Gardaí are skilled at conducting investigations and interviews, and early involvement may prevent the older person being interviewed unnecessarily.

- Gardaí may be able to provide guidance about support services, e.g. Victim Support or Rape Crisis Centres.

- It may be necessary for Gardaí to provide protection for witnesses.

Assessing the needs of the older person

6.33   Once an investigation has established the facts, an assessment of the needs of the older person must be made (basic guidelines on assessment can be found in Appendix G). This assessment will be organised by the Senior Case-Worker and will involve discussion, decision-making and planning for the person's well-being and protection. A case conference may take place and should be organised on the authority of the Dedicated Officer.

6.34   In deciding what action to take, the rights of older people to make choices and take risks and their capacity to make decisions about arrangements for investigating or responding to the abusive situation should be taken into account. Therefore the older person should be included in the assessment process, as a matter of course, unless mental incapacity has been established.

6.35   The older person's capacity is key to decisions about action to be taken. For example, if someone has mental capacity and refuses assistance, this limits the help that he or she can be given; it will not, however, limit the action that may be required to protect others who are at risk. Unless there is evidence to the contrary, older people should be assumed to have the mental capacity to make decisions and give consent. If there is evidence of intimidation, a misuse of authority or undue influence, an assessment of the older person's mental capacity may be necessary.

Making a decision

6.36   One outcome of the investigation and assessment will be the formulation of an agreed care plan for the older person.

6.37   Every effort should be made to involve the older person, his or her carer or family member (if any) and the alleged perpetrator, if appropriate, in both the assessment and planning of his or her future care. However, the older person's wishes with regard to who should be involved must be respected.

6.38   The services recommended by the care plan should be tailored to the needs of the older person. They must be designed to alleviate the stress caused by the abuse. There may be exceptional instances where removal of the older person from his or her home to residential care is both necessary and desirable. In the main, however, the health board should provide care packages that, subject to the wishes of the older person, enable him or her to stay in their own home.

6.39   Crises may give rise to the need for immediate access to services, including residential care. Pending full assessment, health boards must provide appropriate crisis intervention services.

6.40   The relevant service will be responsible for implementing the care plan. Implementation of the care plan should fulfil the requirements of the assessment by providing the most suitable services available. Priority must be given to the prevention of future abuse (guidelines on intervention can be found in Appendix H).

Procedures for dealing with alleged perpetrators

6.41   The alleged perpetrator of elder abuse has a right to know the nature of the allegation(s) made against him or her. If the older person is willing and it is deemed appropriate, and if the alleged perpetrator is willing, he or she should be interviewed in the course of the assessment of an allegation or complaint.

6.42   If the alleged perpetrator is an older person or vulnerable adult or someone with learning disabilities, mental or physical health problems, including substance abuse, he or she may have difficulty participating in the process, in particular, understanding the significance of questions asked or replies given. He or she may therefore need to be assessed and assured of his or her right to the support of an appropriate adult during the investigation.

6.43   Where the interests of the alleged perpetrator and the older person appear to be in conflict, the older person's interests should be paramount. It may be necessary in some cases to provide a separate worker specifically for the alleged perpetrator.

6.44   Family members or carers who are asked to take part in an investigation may be defensive, afraid, angry or aggressive. It may be difficult to get a coherent picture of what is happening. The Senior Case-Worker should have the skills to understand and deal with such situations.

Responsibilities to the alleged perpetrator

6.45   In some circumstances health and social care services may have a responsibility to the alleged perpetrator. This will vary, depending on whether the perpetrator is:

- a member of staff or a contractor
- a member of a recognised professional group
- a relative or spouse or a member of the person's social network
- a carer
- a neighbour or a member of the public
- a person in the care of the health board
- a volunteer or a member of a community group, such as a place of worship or social club
- a person who deliberately targets vulnerable people in order to exploit them.

Alleged perpetrators who are employees

6.46   Service-providers or those who commission services, not only have a duty to the older person who is suffering abuse but also a responsibility to take action in relation to an employee against whom an allegation or complaint has been made. They should therefore ensure that their disciplinary procedures are compatible with the responsibility to protect vulnerable older people.

6.47   If allegations or complaints of elder abuse are made against an employee, he/she should be made aware of his or her rights under employment legislation and under internal disciplinary procedures. He or she may be governed by a code of professional conduct

46

and/or an employment contract, and these may determine the action that can be taken against them. Where appropriate, the employer should report the employee to the body or bodies responsible for professional regulation.

Alleged perpetrators who are relatives, carers or part of the older person's network

6.48 If the alleged perpetrator is a relative or an informal carer or part of the older person's social network, the organisation must balance its duty of care to the older person with the rights of the perpetrator to be told about the complaint or allegation against him or her.

6.49 Once an investigation has been completed, measures can be taken to provide support to the alleged perpetrator.

Budgets

Elder abuse projects allocation per community care area

- All salaries submitted at mid-point + 1 including employer's PRSI

Per community care area

Half-time Dedicated Officer — Grade 8	€30,000
Full-time Senior Case-Worker	€50,000
One full time Clerical Officer — Grade 3	€25,000

TOTAL per Community Care Area	**€105,000**

Overall total to cover all community care areas   *€4,000,000*

National Centre

Director	€75,000
Research/ Education Officer — Grade 7	€45,000
Clerical Officer — Grade 4	€30,000
Library grant	€40,000
IT grant	€60,000
TOTAL	**€250,000**

CHAPTER 8

Prevention

Introduction

8.1 The goal of any response to elder abuse is prevention: primary prevention — stopping elder abuse happening in the first place; and secondary prevention — when it does happen, taking steps to ensure that it does not happen again.

8.2 The response to elder abuse we recommend in this report aims to develop both primary and secondary prevention. It includes the following measures, all of which have been found to be effective in tackling elder abuse elsewhere:

- the development of a new service

- an emphasis on inter-agency co-ordination and multi-disciplinary teams

- the use of advocacy services for older people

- awareness campaigns among the public and among those working with older people

- education and training for all those involved with older people.

8.3 As we noted earlier, the implementation of these measures is merely a first step, a minimum change that will take us only so far in preventing elder abuse. Many barriers remain, barriers that may not be easily overcome in the short term but should nevertheless be the aim of policy in the longer term. Research shows (Gnaedinger, 1989 and Podnieks, 1985) that for a prevention strategy to be effective it is essential that it examines, and continues to analyse the following:

- Ageist attitudes and the devalued status of older people in society.

- Attitudes to violence in the community and in the home.

- The lack of willingness on the part of society in general and health and social workers and carers in particular, to acknowledge that elder abuse happens.

- Budgetary constraints that result in inadequate provision of services for older people and their carers.

- The lack of co-ordination of service provision for older people and their families.

- The lack of specialised education and training for formal and informal carers and for others providing services to older people.

Secondary prevention

8.4 In terms of secondary prevention, although models and tools exist, we have not recommended any of them. There are two reasons for this: firstly, there is no one model or set of tools that is appropriate in all settings or circumstances (McDonald, Pittaway and Nahmiash, 1995); and secondly, the effectiveness of those that are available has yet to be shown. Instead, we offer guidelines from which health and social care providers may develop their own approaches. These set out recommendations for action not only on the part of the service-providers but also on the part of the older person, his or her family and the wider community. They are contained in Appendix G.

Prevention in institutional settings

8.5 Recognising what constitutes good practice, and establishing and maintaining it, is key to the prevention of elder abuse in institutional settings. In institutional settings, as in the wider community, good practice (and therefore the prevention of elder abuse) is not just a matter of the actions of individuals, it is determined, and affected, by a range of inter-related factors, both at the level of the institution and in the wider health and social care system. These include the following:

- legislation and regulations
- policies and procedures for best practice
- the ethos and philosophy of care
- the skills of carers
- the level of support, supervision and training available to carers
- support for older people
- availability of resources.

Legislation, regulations, policies and procedures

8.6 Good practice in residential care settings includes adherence to the relevant legislation and regulations while also adopting policy and operating procedures for the following:

- care planning
- protection of residents' property and valuables
- minimum standards of physical facilities
- confidentiality and privacy
- nursing procedures
- drug administration policies
- activation/participation of residents in the community
- advocacy
- complaints handling, including appeals procedures
- disciplinary procedures.

Ethos and philosophy of care

8.7   The ethos and philosophy of care of the institution should be the recognition of the personal worth and dignity of residents. This ethos must be nurtured by effective leadership, teamwork, education, training and the development of staff. While the *Code of Practice for Nursing Homes 1995* and the *Charter of Rights of Elderly People in Nursing Homes 1997* are not mandatory, they are intended to outline what constitutes high quality care and should be promoted.

Education, training, supervision and support

8.8   The education, training and supervision of staff should actively promote good practice, ensuring that all staff are: aware of elder abuse, know what constitutes good quality care and what is bad practice.

8.9   In addition, education, training and supervision should aim to raise awareness of the need to take personal responsibility for reporting concerns about bad practice and should give staff the skills needed to identify abuse, neglect and mistreatment, including covert, oblique or incipient abuse and to recognise (and be alert and sensitive to) psychological and financial abuse from those outside the institution (external persons and/or agencies).

8.10   It is also essential to ensure that support systems for care staff are in place to help them deal with and alleviate stress.

Support for older people

8.11   Older people themselves must be made aware that certain types of conduct are unacceptable and that some forms of behaviour may be criminal and could result in criminal charges being taken against the abuser. Health and social care workers must listen and talk with older people. If they have any suspicions, they must broach the subject with the older person and provide him or her with appropriate social and legal support.

Resources

8.12   The availability of adequate resources is essential if good quality care is to be provided and elder abuse prevented.

Bibliography

Baumhover L.A and S.C Beall (eds) (1996) *Abuse Neglect and Exploitation of Older Persons —* *Strategies for Assessment and Intervention.* London: Jessica Kingsley Publishers.

Biggs S., C. Phillipson and P. Kingston (1995) *Elder Abuse in Perspective* Buckingham, Open University Press.

Booth B.K, A.A. Bruno and R. Marin (1996) 'Psychological therapy with the abused and neglected patient' in L.A Bauhovers and C.S. Beall (1996) *Abuse Neglect and Exploitation of Older Persons — Strategies for Assessment and Intervention.* London: Jessica Kingsley Publishers.

Cooney, C. and Wrigley, M., (1996) *'Abuse of the elderly with dementia'.* Irish Journal of Psychological Medicine', Vol. 13: 94-96.

Council of Europe (1992), *Violence against Elderly People.* Strasbourg: Council of Europe Press.

Delaney, S., R. Garavan, H. McGee, and A. Tynan, (2001), *Care and Case Management for Older People in Ireland: An outline of current status and a best practice model for service development.* Dublin: National Council on Ageing and Older People.

Department of Health and Children (1990), *Health (Nursing Homes) Act 1990.* Dublin: Stationery Office.

Department of Health and Children (1993), *Nursing Homes Regulations.* Dublin: Stationery Office.

Department of Health and Children (1995), *Code of Practice for Nursing Homes.* Dublin: Stationery Office.

Department of Health and Children (2002*), Quality and Fairness — A Health System for You.* Dublin: Stationery Office.

Department of Health and Children (2002*), Primary Care — A New Direction.* Dublin: Stationery Office.

Department of Health, UK (2000), *No Secrets.* London: HMSO.

Department of Justice (1996), *Domestic Violence Act.* Dublin: Stationery Office.

Garavan, R., H. McGee, R. Winder (2001), *Health and Social Services for Older People (HeSSOP) Consulting older people on health and social services: A survey of service use, experiences and needs.* Dublin: National Council on Ageing and Older People.

Gnaedinger, N. J. (1989), *Elder Abuse: A Discussion Paper.* Ottawa: Health and Welfare Canada.

Irish Registered Nursing Homes Association (1997), *Charter of the Rights of Elderly People Accommodated in Nursing Homes.* Dublin: Irish Registered Nursing Homes Association.

Horkan, E.M. (1995), 'Elder abuse in the Republic of Ireland' in Kosberg, J.L. and J.L. Garcia (eds), *Elder Abuse: International and Cross-Culture Perspectives.* London: Sage.

Kingston P, B. Penhale (1994) 'Recognition of a major problem: assessment and management of elder abuse and neglect' *Professional Nurse* 9(5): 343-347.

Kingston P. and A. Reay (1996), 'Elder Abuse And Neglect' in R.T. Woods (1996). *Handbook of the Clinical Psychology of Ageing,* Chichester: John Wiley & Sons.

McCreadie C. (2000), *No Secrets: meaning and implementation.* Journal of Adult Protection 2 (3) 5-16.

McDonald, L., E. Pittaway, and D. Nahmiash (1995), 'Issues in practice with respect to mistreatment of older people'. In M. J. MacLean (ed.), *Abuse & Neglect of Older Canadians: Strategies for Change.* Toronto: Thompson Educational Publishing, Inc., (pp. 5-16).

National Council on Ageing and Older People (2000), *Framework for Quality in Long-Term Residential Care for Older People in Ireland.* Dublin: National Council on Ageing and Older People.

O'Neill, D., P. Mc Cormack, T.B. Walsh, and D. Coakely (1990), 'Elder Abuse'. *Irish Journal of Medical Science,* Vol. 159: 48-49.

O'Loughlin, A. (1990) 'Old Age Abuse in the domestic setting: definition and identification'. *Irish Social Worker,* Vol. 9: 4-7.

O'Loughlin, A., and J. Duggan (1998), *Abuse, Neglect and Mistreatment of Older People: An Exploratory Study.* Dublin: National Council on Ageing and Older People.

O'Shea, E., and S. O'Reilly (1999), An *Action Plan for Dementia.* Dublin: National Council on Ageing and Older People.

O'Shea, E., (2000), *The Costs of Caring for People with Dementia and Related Cognitive Impairments.* Dublin: National Council on Ageing and Older People.

Podnieks, E., and E. Baillie (1995), 'Education as the key to the prevention of elder abuse and neglect'. In M. J. MacLean (ed.), *Abuse & Neglect of Older Canadians: Strategies for Change.* Toronto: Thompson Educational Publishing, Inc, (pp. 81-93).

Ruddle, H., F. O'Donoghue, R Mulvihill (1997), *The Years Ahead Report: A Review of the Implementation of Its Recommendations.* Dublin: National Council on Ageing and Older People.

Woods R.T. (1996) *Handbook of the Clinical Psychology of Ageing* Chichester: John Wiley & Sons.

Appendix A

Submissions Summary

On foot of the following call for submissions on elder abuse in May 2000, we received the following submissions:

WORKING GROUP ON ELDER ABUSE

Call for Submissions

Following a report of the National Council on Ageing and Older People entitled *Abuse, Neglect, and Mistreatment of Older People,* a Working Group on Elder Abuse has been established by Dr Tom Moffatt TD, Minister of State at the Department of Health and Children with special responsibility for older people. The Working Group will advise on the development of policies, procedures and guidelines in relation to elder abuse.

The Working Group welcomes submissions from interested groups or individuals on how policies, procedures and guidelines, for the detection and management of elder abuse, can best be developed.

Please forward submissions in writing, in braille, on tape, on disk or other format to:

The Research Officer, Working Group on Elder Abuse, 58 Fitzwilliam Square, Dublin 2, Tel: 01 676 0944
Fax: 01 676 5288, E-mail: deirdre@wgea.ie

Closing date for submissions is 12 May 2000
Submissions will be accessible under the Freedom of Information Act 1997

The Working Group on Elder Abuse received a total of 62 written submissions. Of these 62 submissions, 33 were from individuals and 29 were from health and social care professionals and organisations.

The **majority of individual submissions** concentrate on describing the personal experience of a person known to the submitter rather than on making recommendations as to how elder abuse should be redressed. Thus, they provide insight into perceptions and experiences of abuse in various forms and in various situations in Ireland.

A number of **submissions from organisations** also focus on the personal dimension of elder abuse. The majority, however, are less subjective. They tend, on the whole, to adopt a case-study approach, focusing on the wider picture, on definitional aspects of elder abuse and its implications for policy changes. Many offer recommendations on how elder abuse should be addressed (on which there appears to be considerable agreement).

A summary of the recommendations offered by all those making a submission is given below.

Recommendations

1. **Increase in staffing levels in care facilities for older people**

   - An increase in the number of home helps.

   - An increase in the number of nursing aides.

2. **Allocation/Reallocation/Creation of new roles**

   - Allocation of social workers responsible for older people in each health board.

   - The appointment of 'a new class of nurse' responsible for older people (separate but complementary to the role of the Public Health Nurse).

   - A more prominent role for the Gardaí in the protection of older people.

3. **Education and Training**

   - Formal training and education for nursing aides and home helps in the care of older people.

   - Up-to-date information for carers regarding drugs and research issues affecting older people.

   - Coverage on television and radio on elder abuse.

   - The incorporation of abuse modules into various professional and academic courses.

   - The implementation of an education programme for children, focusing on their attitudes to older people.

   - An increase in the awareness of elder abuse among health and social care workers.

4. **Additional services for older people**

   - Transport.

   - Programmes to alleviate the poverty and isolation of older people.

   - An increase in the number of day care centres.

   - An increase in medical entitlements.

   - An increase in banking privileges.

   - Free legal aid for all older people.

   - Maintain and extend the Meals-on-Wheels service.

5. Counselling and support for carers

- An increase in Home Help hours (from one hour limitation per day).

- Specialist talks and information to be made available through support groups, for carers looking after older people with specific health problems such as Dementia.

- Preparatory and training programmes for those anticipating becoming a carer.

6. Clarification of the roles and responsibilities, authority and accountability of professionals involved in care of older people

7. Identifying risk factors and situations of elder abuse

- Proper monitoring and supervision structures in nursing homes for the detection of elder abuse.

- The establishment of a national register of elder abuse offenders.

- All staff caring for older people to be subject to full employment history checks and Garda checks.

Submissions from individuals: Domestic abuse

Victims of elder abuse in domestic settings did not provide submissions to the Working Group on Elder Abuse. Four submissions referring to domestic abuse were received. Of these, two came from a relative of the abused, with one claiming that the suspected perpetrator of abuse is a family member, while the other is a carer outside of the family.

The remaining two submissions were from those who claim to be familiar with particular cases of domestic abuse. A member of the family was the perpetrator in each abuse case, with the exception of one where a carer outside of the family is suspected.

All four submissions include financial abuse and general neglect. Three instances of abuse occur in a rural setting, while the other occurs in an urban setting.

Submissions from individuals: Institutional abuse

Six individuals offered submissions relating to institutional abuse. Their areas of concern include:

- Lack of toilet and shower facilities.

- Neglect, degrading conditions, overcrowding and lack of privacy.

- Noise and absence of therapies.

- Lack of privacy and increasing spread of mixed-sex wards.

- Neglect, sociological abuse and the mismanagement of medication.

- Physical, verbal, financial, and psychological abuse.

Victims of elder abuse in institutional settings did not provide any submissions. However, there were six submissions from individuals who have indirect experiences of elder abuse in an institutional setting.

Five of these are from relatives of the older person in a nursing home and the other from a nurse who wrote in a personal capacity about her experience of elder abuse in the nursing home in which she worked.

Complaints of abuse include physical abuse, verbal abuse, financial abuse, psychological abuse, sociological abuse and neglect. Neglect was the most frequently cited, ranging from claims of overcrowding, noise, lack of privacy, mismanagement of medication (both under-and over-medication) and lack of toilet and shower facilities.

The majority of submissions place the cause of institutional abuse on the lack of nursing staff and conditions in the nursing home, while recognising the work burden on nursing staff. They suggest an increase in the number of nursing staff and an expansion of the work remit of the nursing aides to prevent such abuse occurring.

In cases of physical and verbal abuse, individual submissions assign the blame to individual members of staff. Recommendations to prevent such abuse occurring include an increase in the awareness of abuse, the establishment of telephone help-lines, an inquiry into how nursing homes are run, an Inspectorate for all nursing homes, and compensation for grievances suffered.

Submissions from professionals: First-hand experience of elder abuse

Seven professionals had direct experience of elder abuse. These included Public Health Nurses, General Nurses, Doctors and a Community Organisation.

The majority of submissions, those from nurses and the community organisation tell of abuse in a rural setting, one relating to institutional abuse and the other in a domestic or community setting. They also tell of increasing caregiver stress, the inadequate living conditions of older people, financial abuse psychological abuse and neglect by relatives.

The General Practitioner is witnessing increasing incidents of elder neglect in the community.

A nurse in a public nursing home describes the incidence of institutional abuse in detail. The abuse includes physical abuse, psychological abuse and neglect, which includes over-sedation, shouting at patients, the indiscriminate use of rectal enemas and taking money from patients (this anonymous submission was referred by the Working Group on Elder Abuse to the appropriate health board).

Submissions from professionals: Indirect experience of elder abuse

Many submissions contain detailed recommendations on policy, procedure and guideline development.

Although there are considerable overlaps in the type of recommendations, each of the professional organisations have particular grievances that they believe require urgent action. The majority of these recommendations are applicable to their profession.

Those submissions based in a *rural setting* tend to focus more on the needs of older people in community settings, whereas those submissions from an *urban setting* tend to focus on improving the welfare of residents in nursing homes.

Pilot Project Proposal

Following a report of the National Council on Ageing and Older People entitled *Abuse, Neglect, and Mistreatment of Older People*, a Working Group on Elder Abuse has been established, under the aegis of the National Council on Ageing and Older People, by Dr Tom Moffatt TD, Minister of State at the Department of Health and Children with special responsibility for older people. The Minister has appointed Dr. Desmond O'Neill Chairperson of the Working Group. The Working Group will advise on the development of policies, procedures and guidelines in relation to elder abuse. These will provide support for health boards and their staff in the prevention, detection and management of elder abuse.

Draft policies and procedures have been prepared by the Working Group and it is proposed that pilot projects be established in two health board areas to test and evaluate them.

Purpose

The main purpose of the pilot study is therefore to assess the effectiveness of the draft policies and procedures on elder abuse, in two health board areas. A pilot project area would preferably be a community care area, with a hospital attached and long-term institutional care for older people provided.

It is anticipated that the pilot projects will create a framework of action within which all responsible agencies can work together to ensure a consistent and effective response to any circumstances giving ground for concern about elder abuse.

Additional aims of the pilot projects are to:

- Implement draft policies, procedures and guidelines for the assessment, identification and intervention in cases of elder abuse. The policies and protocols will ensure a consistent response among agencies to cases of elder abuse.

- Create a context in which older people and those concerned about the abuse of older people can disclose their concerns and receive an appropriate response.

- Detect instances of unmet need for service development.

- Contribute to the formulation of national policies and procedures on elder abuse.

61

The Policies and Procedures

The purpose of the elder abuse policies and procedures is to promote good practice in responding to cases or suspected cases of elder abuse as they arise. Policies and procedures cover the following:

- Overall guidance, including definitions, identification, legal framework and risk factors.
- Procedures for making, receiving and processing elder abuse referrals.
- Assessment.
- Decision-making on intervention and action.
- Investigation.
- Intervention, including planning for the person's future and their protection.
- Record-keeping.
- Procedures relating to the alleged perpetrator.
- Disciplinary procedures for staff members when a health worker is alleged to be responsible for abuse.
- Criminal proceedings.

The Pilot Projects

The pilot projects will include:

- A *training strategy* to sensitise all staff to the existence of elder abuse and the complexity of elder abuse cases which arise. A training programme is being designed to provide information on elder abuse and to increase awareness and understanding of elder abuse issues. It will include a definition of elder abuse and information on the detection and on the legal context and policies on elder abuse in Ireland. It will also include guidelines for each relevant profession.
- A *programme to develop awareness* of the projects and of elder abuse itself among all health care staff in the health board area.
- *The introduction of the draft elder abuse policies, procedures and guidelines,* as outlined in the manual, in the pilot project areas.
- *Monitoring* of volume and outcomes, impact and resource implications of older persons' protection work.
- *Evaluation* of staff awareness levels before, during and after training, and an evaluation of the effectiveness of the draft policies, procedures and guidelines implemented in the pilot projects areas.

Staff Involvement

The proposal makes provision for the following mechanisms to ensure the success of the projects in the pilot areas: *an Elder Abuse Officer, a Policy Development and Implementation Committee and a Senior Case-Worker for Elder Abuse.*

- **The Elder Abuse Officer** will be a position at managerial level, with experience in service delivery to older people. The Elder Abuse Officer will be responsible for the development and implementation of the health board's response to elder abuse in the pilot project area.

- The Elder Abuse Officer will be supported by the **Policy Development and Implementation Committee** of the health board which will bring together representatives of services to older people as well as other bodies such as the Gardaí.

- Responsibility for the assessment of suspected cases of elder abuse referred to the health board will fall to a **Senior Case-Worker for Elder Abuse.** This practitioner may be a social worker or nurse with appropriate expertise and training. Assessments will be undertaken in conjunction with appropriate service-providers within the health board.

The Training Programme

The Working Group on Elder Abuse will commission a trainer to design and conduct a training programme for the pilot projects in the two community care areas selected. The training will encompass:

- Two days of intensive training on elder abuse policies and procedures as listed above. This will be provided to three to four persons from each of the professional groups listed below.

- An inservice training session will also be provided to the remaining health and social care staff, again listed below.

Training will be delivered to the following groups:

Community care management and professions:	General Area Managers Public Health Nurses Public Health Superintendents Gardaí Housing Welfare Officers Practice Nurses Community Welfare Officers Therapists
Institutional care management and professions:	Nurses in Accident and Emergency and Nursing Homes Social Workers Hospital Administrator
Care assistants and home helps:	Residential and domestic Home Helps and their organisers
Doctors:	General Practitioners and Geriatricians

Time Frame

The pilot projects will be conducted in two health board areas. They will begin in January 2001 and continue until 30 September 2001.

1. The **training programme** will begin in January 2001 until 31 March 2001, and it will take place in a community care area of two health board regions.

2. The draft **policies, procedures and guidelines** on elder abuse will be introduced in two pilot areas on 1 April 2001 and will remain in force to 30 September 2001.

3. **Evaluation:** The pilot projects will be monitored and evaluated by a qualified researcher to be appointed by the Working Group on Elder Abuse.

Grant

Subject to its 2001 financial allocation, the Working Group on Elder Abuse, through the National Council on Ageing and Older People, will provide a grant towards the costs of the pilot projects in the two community care areas, including the appointment of the Senior Case-Worker. These costs will be agreed with a senior representative of the health boards.

Future reference

For further clarification on the pilot projects, please do not hesitate to contact: Deirdre Fitzpatrick, Research Officer Working Group on Elder Abuse, Working Group on Elder Abuse 58 Fitzwilliam Square, Dublin 2. Tel: 01 676 0944, Fax: 01 676 5288, E-mail: deirdre@wgea.ie

Training Brief

Background

Following a report of the National Council on Ageing and Older People entitled *Abuse, Neglect, and Mistreatment of Older People,* a Working Group on Elder Abuse has been established by Dr. Tom Moffatt TD, Minister of State at the Department of Health and Children with special responsibility for older people.

The Working Group has prepared draft policies, procedures and guidelines on elder abuse. These will be introduced on a pilot basis in two health board community care areas. The pilot projects will commence in December 2000 and run until September 2001.

The main purpose of the pilot study is to assess the effectiveness of the draft policies and procedures on elder abuse in the two community care areas. It is anticipated that the pilot projects will create a framework of action within which all responsible agencies can work together to ensure a consistent and effective response to any circumstances giving ground for concern about elder abuse.

The Working Group is presently seeking trainers with expertise in health and/or social care to design a training programme on elder abuse and deliver the programme to a range of health care professionals in the community care areas.

Training Objectives

The training programme will seek to increase awareness of elder abuse and neglect among both care staff and other relevant professionals. It will also aim to assist them in determining how best to respond sensitively and appropriately to cases or suspected cases of elder abuse as they arise in the course of their work. This will entail educating professionals and those involved in elder care about:

- The prevalence and the extent of elder abuse.

- Understanding the social context of abuse and neglect of the elderly and how to identify high-risk factors and the underlying causes of elder abuse.

- The critical role played by service providers who work with older people and how they can become actively involved in the prevention, detection and management of elder abuse.

- The learning of appropriate policies, procedures and interventions to ensure effective responses to elder abuse as it arises or is suspected.

The purpose of the training programme is to ensure that service-providers from different disciplines, backgrounds and job settings are sensitised to the issue of elder abuse, that they are able to identify abuse and neglect of the elderly, that they learn to handle cases of elder abuse sensitively, and make referrals when appropriate, to designated persons or agencies.

The training programme will ensure that the problem of elder abuse becomes more widely acknowledged, skills become sharpened and cases of elder abuse are handled more sensitively. It will also help people to recognise the scope of the problem and to begin to search for solutions.

Framework for Training Programme

a. **Design of the Training Programme:**

To ensure that the training programme on elder abuse is of maximum use to the health and social care professionals, it is necessary that the programme is designed to examine the following issues:

1. *Definition and awareness of elder abuse, including:*

- The nature of elder abuse.

- Attitudes to older people and ageism.

- The frequency with which elder abuse occurs.

- The effects of elder abuse on victims, perpetrators, and society as a whole.

- Understanding cultural variations of elder abuse.

2. *Detection of elder abuse, including the:*

- Identification of signs that an older adult has been abused.

- Risk factors for elder abuse.

- Factors affecting the assessment of abuse — risk factors, capacity and consent.

3. *Legal context and policy of elder abuse in Ireland, including the:*

- Legal framework – format to follow.

- Government and health board policy on elder care.

- The Working Group on Elder Abuse's draft policy on elder abuse.

4. *Procedures to be followed in cases or suspected cases of elder abuse, including:*

- Identification of appropriate resources and services for older adults who have been abused.

- Referral procedures.

- Working Group on Elder Abuse draft procedures on elder abuse.

5. *Individual professional guidelines*

b. **Professionals involved in the training**

The training programme will be conducted in a community care area of two health board regions. Trainers will be expected to design and deliver a training programme to match the educational needs of the following key groups:

Community health and social care professionals:	Public Health Nurses
	General Practitioners
	Gardaí
	Housing Welfare Officers
	General Area Managers
	Practice Nurses
	Community Welfare Officers
	Therapists
	Area Medical Officers
Hospital health and social care professionals:	Nurses in Accident and Emergency and Nursing Homes
	Social Workers
	Hospital Administrators
	Psychiatric Nurses
	Heads of Departments
	Day Centre Co-ordinators and personnel
	Geriatricians
	Psychiatrists and Psychiatrists of Old Age
	Accident and Emergency staff
	Therapists
	Hospital Specialists
Care assistants and home helps:	Residential and domestic settings
	Home Helps and their organisers
Financial and legal representatives:	Legal agents of health boards
	Customer service representatives from banks
	Solicitors

The programme will be designed in conjunction with the Working Group on Elder Abuse. The training manual will be subject to the approval of the Working Group at all times.

c. **Stages in the training programme**

Training will be designed, organised and provided at two levels of intensity and detail as follows:

- Two days of intensive training encompassing all the issues listed at (a) above will be provided to selected individuals from each of the professional groups listed at (b) above.

- Half-day inservice general training sessions will be provided to the remaining health and social care staff in the professional groups listed at (b) above.

All training will be organised to ensure that the numbers attending sessions are not too great for educational purposes.

Main Training Tasks

In view of the sensitive nature of elder abuse, the Working Group requires that training sessions be conducted by two people on all occasions. Trainers will be expected to:

a. **Design a training programme on elder abuse**

- Develop training objectives

- Develop a training curriculum in consultation with the Working Group.

b. **Arrange the training programme in the health boards**

- It will be necessary that the trainers/training team liaise closely with the appointed member of the health boards to make arrangements on the establishment of the training programme on elder abuse in the community care areas. This will include agreement on training times, training places and the health and social care staff to be included in the training.

c. **Deliver training on elder abuse**

- Create an effective learning environment.

- Employ training methods, which maximise the active participation of those attending.

- Deliver training to the groups listed above.

- Deliver training to groups in sessions of manageable numbers.

d. **Liaise with the Evaluator**

- The pilot projects will be monitored and evaluated by a qualified researcher to be appointed by the Working Group. It will be important from the outset that trainers agree with the evaluator appropriate mechanisms to record, monitor and evaluate the experience of the training aspects of the programme.

e. **Report writing**

- Trainers will be required to provide a report of their experiences of the training programme on its completion to the Working Group on Elder Abuse.

Characteristics of the training team

Trainers should have a strong background in health and social care training and be familiar with motivational and learning theory and techniques in this field. Experience of training professionals in regard to elder abuse or other matters relating to the welfare of older people will be an asset.

Additional skills required include the following:

- Good communication and interpersonal skills
- Teaching ability
- Facilitation skills — individual and group
- Extensive knowledge of the health and social services available to older people in Ireland
- Sufficient support and time resources to carry out the training programme in the two community care areas.

Working arrangements

Subject to appropriate approvals, secondment may be arranged to design and conduct the training programme.

Time

It is proposed that the training programme be commissioned as soon as possible with a view to initiating the work in December 2000 and completing it in April 2001.

Proposals

The Working Group on Elder Abuse invites qualified candidates to submit tenders for the training programme on elder abuse. Proposals should be received no later than 27 October 2000. The tender should provide a detailed outline of the steps that will be taken to achieve the main project tasks. A timeframe and itemised costing for the project should also be included.

Further reference

For further information or clarification of the training brief, please do not hesitate to contact Deirdre Fitzpatrick, Research Officer, Working Group on Elder Abuse, 58 Fitzwilliam Square, Dublin 2, Tel: 01 676 0944, Fax: 01 676 5288, E-mail: deirdre@wgea.ie

Evaluation Brief

Background

Following a report of the National Council on Ageing and Older People, entitled *Abuse, Neglect, and Mistreatment of Older People: An Exploratory Study*, a Working Group on Elder Abuse has been established, under the aegis of the National Council on Ageing and Older People, by Dr. Tom Moffatt TD, Minister of State at the Department of Health and Children who has special responsibility for older people.

The Working Group has prepared draft policies, procedures and guidelines for the identification, assessment and management of elder abuse. These will be introduced on a pilot basis in two health board community care areas following the completion of a training programme for health care staff and other relevant professionals in the pilot areas.

It is anticipated that the training programme and the implementation of the draft policies, procedures and guidelines will create a framework of action within which all responsible persons and agencies can work together to ensure a consistent and effective response to any circumstances giving ground for concern about elder abuse.

The Working Group proposes to commission an evaluation of the pilot projects to assess the effectiveness of the training programme and of the draft policies, procedures and guidelines on elder abuse in the community care areas. It therefore seeks proposals for an evaluation which will:

- Assess the effectiveness of the training programme in achieving its objectives.

- Assess the effectiveness of the draft policies, procedures and guidelines for promoting best practice in the identification, assessment and management of elder abuse in the pilot areas.

- Assist in the development of national policies, procedures and guidelines on elder abuse in Ireland.

What Is To Be Evaluated?

1. The training programme

The purpose of the training programme is to increase awareness of elder abuse and neglect among both care staff and other relevant professionals. It will also aim to assist them to determine how best to respond sensitively and appropriately to cases or suspected cases of elder abuse as they arise in the course of their work. The training programme will ensure that the problem of elder abuse becomes more widely acknowledged, skills become sharpened and cases of elder abuse are handled more sensitively. It will also help people to recognise the scope of the problem and to begin to search for solutions. This will entail educating professionals and those involved in elder care about:

- The definition of elder abuse.

- The prevalence of elder abuse and the extent of the problem.

- Identification of elder abuse.

- Understanding the social context of abuse and neglect of the elderly and learn to identify high-risk factors and the underlying causes of elder abuse.

- The critical role played by service-providers who work with older people and how they can become actively involved in the solution.

- Learning appropriate interventions and available community resources and contact names.

- Legal context and policy of elder abuse in Ireland.

- Procedures for suspected elder abuse cases.

- Individual professional guidelines.

Training will be provided to community health and social care professionals, hospital health and social care professionals, care assistants and home helps, and financial and legal representatives in the health boards.

Two days of intensive training encompassing all the issues listed above will be provided to selected individuals from each of the professional groups and a half-day inservice general training session will be provided to the remaining health and social care staff in the professional groups.

2.   The Draft Policies Procedures and Guidelines

The purpose of elder abuse policies, procedures and guidelines is to promote good practice in responding to cases or suspected cases of elder abuse as they arise. The policies, procedures and guidelines cover the following:

- Overall guidance including definitions, identification, legal framework and risk factors of elder abuse.

- Procedures for making, receiving and processing suspected elder abuse referrals.

- Assessment of suspected elder abuse cases.

- Decision-making on intervention and action in suspected elder abuse cases.

- Investigation of suspected elder abuse cases.

- Intervention, including planning for the abused person's future and for their protection.

- Record-keeping of suspected elder abuse.

- Procedures relating to the alleged perpetrator.

- Disciplinary procedures for staff members when a health care worker is alleged to be responsible for abuse.

- Criminal proceedings in suspected elder abuse.

Framework for the Evaluation:

Pilot project schedule

1. The implementation of the training programme (January – April 2001).

2. The implementation of the policies, procedures and guidelines on elder abuse (April – September 2001).

3. Evaluation of staff awareness levels prior to, during and after training and an evaluation of the effectiveness of the draft policies, procedures and guidelines implemented in the pilot project areas (January – September 2001).

4. Monitoring of volume and outcomes, impact and resource implications of older persons' protection work (April – September 2001).

5. Preparation of draft evaluation report of the pilot projects (September – November 2001).

Characteristics of the Evaluator

Evaluator(s) should have a strong background in the evaluation of health care projects. Experience in the evaluation of elder abuse issues or other matters relating to the welfare of older people will be an advantage.

Interpersonal skills

The evaluators will be required to liaise closely with the Working Group and with the health board committees, officials and representatives. An ability to work co-operatively and openly with both committees and individuals will be important to ensure that the objectives of the evaluation are realised. Good communication at all levels will be required to foster an appreciation of the objectives of the evaluation and to ensure that ownership in the achievement of these objectives is shared. The views of parties at all levels of the project, including those of the Working Group itself should be reflected in the final evaluation report.

Additional skills required include the following:

- A good knowledge of evaluation methodologies.

- A proven record of commissioned evaluation projects.

- Research and analytical skills.

- Presentation and report writing skills.

Further Information — Managing The Evaluation

Monitoring

Progress reports will be required at key stages in the evaluation at monthly intervals. These reports should be short, two sides of A4. In the event where major changes to the evaluation are required while it is in progress, the Working Group must be consulted.

The Working Group will ensure that it:

- Develops a partnership with the evaluator based on regular liaison.

- Prepares information for the evaluator(s) in advance of it being needed.

- Identifies and informs the evaluator of any changes in requirements, particularly any changes in management needs for the evaluation.

Time

It is proposed that the evaluation be commissioned as soon as possible with a view to initiating the work in January 2001 and completing it in November 2001.

Proposals

The Working Group invites qualified candidates to submit proposals on the evaluation to be received no later than 14 November 2000. The tender should provide a detailed outline of the steps that will be taken to achieve the main project tasks. A timeframe and itemised costing for the project should also be included.

Further reference

For further information or clarification of the training brief, please do not hesitate to contact Deirdre Fitzpatrick, Research Officer, Working Group on Elder Abuse, 58 Fitzwilliam Square, Dublin 2, Tel: 01 676 0944, Fax: 01 676 5288, E-mail: deirdre@wgea.ie

Some Potential Indicators of Elder Abuse

Psychological Abuse	Neglect	Financial Abuse	Physical Abuse	Sexual Abuse
• Demoralisation • Depression • Feelings of Hopelessness/Helplessness • Disrupted Appetites/Sleeping Patterns • Tearfulness • Excessive Fears • Agitation • Resignation • Confusion • Unexplained paranoia • Strong ambivalent feelings towards the abuser	• Dehydration • Malnutrition • Inappropriate clothing • Poor hygiene • Unkempt appearance • Under/over medication • Unattended medical needs • Exposure to danger/lack of supervision • Absence of required aids, including glasses, dentures. • Pressure sores	• Unexplained or sudden inability to pay bills • Unexplained or sudden withdrawal of money from accounts • Funds diverted for someone else's use • Damage to property • Unexplained disappearance of possessions • No funds for food, clothes, services • Absence of required aids, medication • Refusal to spend money • Disparity between living conditions and assets • Extraordinary interest by family member in older people's assets • Making dramatic financial decisions	• Bruises (on different surface areas; may reflect shape of a weapon; whether clustered or not) • Laceration (particularly to mouth, lips, gums, eyes, ears) • Abrasions • Scratches • Burns (inflicted by cigarettes, matches, rope, iron, immersion in hot water) • Sprains • Dislocations, fractures • Marks left by a gag • Hair loss (possible hair-pulling) • Missing teeth • Eye injuries (black eye, detached retina)	• Trauma about the genitals, breasts, rectum, mouth • Injury to face, neck, chest, abdomen, thighs, buttocks • Presence of sexually transmitted disease • Human bite marks

Steering Group Membership

Steering group members may be selected from the following health and social care workers

Community health and social care professionals

Public Health Nurses
General Practitioners
Gardaí
Housing Welfare Officers
General Area Managers
Practice Nurses
Community Welfare Officers
Occupational Therapists
Physiotherapists
Psychologists
Area Medical Officers

Hospital health and social care professionals

Nurses in Accident and Emergency departments and Nursing Homes
Social Workers
Hospital Administrators
Psychiatric Nurses
Heads of Departments
Day Centre Co-ordinators and personnel
Geriatricians
Psychiatrists and Psychiatrists of Old Age
Accident and Emergency department staff
Occupational Therapists
Physiotherapists
Psychologists
Hospital Specialists

Care assistants and home helps

Residential and domestic
Home Helps and their organisers

Financial and legal representatives

Legal agents of health boards
Bank customer service representatives
Solicitors

Appendix F

Sources of information and advice

Irish Organisations

Age and Opportunity, Marino Institute of Education, Griffith Avenue, Dublin 9, Tel: 805 7709, Fax: 853 5117, Email ageandop@mie.ie

The Carers Association, Metropole Centre, James Street, Kilkenny, Tel: (056) 21188/21424, Fax: (056) 21446/53531, Email: director@carersireland.com

Irish Association of Older People, Room B15, University College, Earlsfort Terrace, Dublin 2, Tel: 475 0013, Fax: 475 0071, Email: iaop@oceanfree.net

National Council On Ageing and Older People, 22 Clanwilliam Square, Grand Canal Quay, Dublin 2, Tel: 01 676 6484, Fax: 01 676 5754, http://www.ncaop.ie

Third Age Active Retirement Group Summerhill Ireland, Third Age Centre, Summerhill, County Meath, Phone/Fax Number: +353 (0) 405 57766, Senior Help Line 1850 440 444, Email info@thirdage-ireland.com, http://www.thirdage-ireland.com/

Professional Associations and Trade Unions

Irish College of General Practitioners, 4-5 Lincoln Place, Dublin 2, Tel: 676 3705
Fax: 676 5850, Email: info@icgp.ie, http://www.icgp.ie

Irish Medical Organisation, 10 Fitzwilliam Place, Dublin 2, Tel: 676 7273, http://www.imo.ie

Irish Nursing Organisation, 11 Fitzwilliam Place, Dublin 2, Tel: 676 0137, Fax: 661 0466, Email: ino@ino.ie, http://www.ino.ie

Irish Association of Old Age Psychiatry, Dr Colm Cooney (Chairman), St Vincent's Hospital, Elm Park, Dublin 4.

Irish Association of Physician and Geriatric Medicine, Dr J.B. Walsh (Chairman), St James Hospital, Dublin 8. Tel: 146 2618

Irish Association of Social Workers, 114-116 Pearse Street, Dublin 2, Telephone (+353 1) 677 4838 Facsimile (+353 1) 671 5734, Email: iasw@iol.ie, http://www.iasw.eire.org

Office of the Ombudsman, 18 Lower Leeson Street, Dublin 2, Tel: 678 5222, Fax: 639 5689, http://www.irlgov.ie/ombudsman

Psychological Society of Ireland, CX House, 2A Corn Exchange Place, Poolbeg Street, Dublin 2, Tel: 01 671 7122

An Bord Altranais, The Nursing Board, 31-32 Fitzwilliam Square, Dublin 2, Tel: 639 8500, Fax: 676 3348, Email: admin@nursingboard.ie, http://www.nursingboard.ie

Comhairle (formerly the National Social Services Board) | Hume House, Ballsbridge Dublin 4, Tel: 605 9000, Fax: 605 9099, Email: comhairle@comhairle.ie, http://www.comhairle.ie

United Kingdom

Action on Elder Abuse, Astral House, 1268 London Road, London SW16 ER.
Tel (++44) (0) 20 8765 7000 Fax: (++44) (0)20 8679 4074, Email: aea@ace.org.uk,
http://www.elderabuse.org.uk/

Advocacy across London http://home.btconnect.com/aal/

Age Concern England http://www.ace.org.uk/

Age Concern Institute of Gerontology http://www.kcl.ac.uk/kis/schools/life_sciences/health/gerontology/top.html

Alcohol Concern http://www.alcoholconcern.org.uk/

Ann Craft Trust http://www.nottingham.ac.uk/sociology/act/

Arthritis Care http://www.arthritiscare.org.uk/

Brendon Care http://www.brendoncare.org.uk/

British Association for Service to the Elderly http://www.base.org.uk/

Care Directions http://www.caredirections.co.uk/

Carers National Association http://www.carersuk.demon.co.uk

Caring Matters http://www.caringmatters.dial.pipex.com/

Centre for Policy on Ageing http://www.cpa.org.uk/index.html

Citizens Advice Bureau http://www.nacab.org.uk

Commission for Health Improvement http://www.chi.nhs.uk/

Counsel and Care http://www.counselandcare.org.uk/

Darlington Domestic Violence Unit http://www.ddvf.org/

Department of Health, Richmond House, 79 Whitehall, London SW1A 2NS, Tel: 0207 210 4850, Email dhmail@doh.gsi.gov.uk

Dementia Web http://www.ddvf.org/

Disability Rights Commission http://www.dlf.org.uk/

Disabled Living Foundation http://www.dlf.org.uk/

Friends of the Elderly http://www.fote.org.uk/

Government Carer Information http://www.doh.gov.uk/carers/

Health Care Information http://www.doh.gov.uk/carers/

Help the Aged http://www.doh.gov.uk/carers/

International Network for Prevention of Elderly Abuse http://www.doh.gov.uk/carers/

Knowsley Social Services http://www.knowsley.gov.uk/social/older_people/strategy/elderabuse.html

National Institute of Clinical Excellence (NICE) http://www.knowsley.gov.uk/social/older_people/ strategy elderabuse.html

Oxford Dementia Centre http://www.knowsley.gov.uk/social/older_people/strategy/elderabuse.html

Patients Association http://www.patients-association.com/intro.htm

Pavilion http://www.pavpub.com/pavpub/home/index.asp

Prevention of Professional Abuse Network http://www.popan.org.uk/

Public Concern at Work http://www.pcaw.co.uk/

Public Guardianship Office http://www.publictrust.gov.uk/

Royal College of Psychiatrists http://www.rcpsych.ac.uk/

Royal United Kingdom Beneficent Association http://www.rukba.org.uk/

Scottish Office of the Public Guardian http://www.publicguardian-scotland.gov.uk

Twylife http://www.twylife.com/

Victim Support http://www.vslambeth.org.uk/

Women's Aid http://www.womensaid.org.uk/

America

Alcohol and elder abuse (http://www.agingincanada.ca/Seniors%20Alcohol/1e6.htm)

American Bar Association Commission on Domestic Violence http://www.abanet.org/domviol /home.html)

Article, "Elder Abuse and Neglect" (http://www.webster.edu/~woolflm/abuse.html)

Articles: "Elder Abuse in the Domestic Setting," "Elder Abuse in the Institutional Setting," and "Elder Abuse: Financial Exploitation by a Conservator" http://www.ink.org/public/ keln/bibs /bibindex.html)

Domestic Violence Internet Project (http://www.growing.com/nonviolent)

Elder Abuse Prevention: A Consortium Serving Alameda and Contra Costa Counties in California, USA. http://www.oaktrees.org/elder/

Elder Law Issues (http://www.elder-law.com/issues.html)

Family Caregiver Alliance (http://www.caregiver.org/index.html)

Indiana, Clark County: The Clark County Prosecuting Attorney (http://www.clarkprosecutor.org/html/aps/aps.htm)

Massachusetts, Brockton: Senior Protection Team
(http://www.state.ma.us/da/plymouth/fampro/senior/senproteam.htm)

Mental Health: National Technical Assistance Centre for State Mental Health Planning (NTAC)
(http:// www.nasmhpd.org/ntac/index.htm)

Minnesota Centre against Violence and Abuse (http://www.mincava.umn.edu/)

National Ageing Information Centre (http://www.aoa.dhhs.gov/naic)

National Centre for Victims of Crime (NCVC) (http://www.ncvc.org)

National Citizens' Coalition for Nursing Home Reform (http://www.nccnhr.org/)

The National Elder Abuse Incidence Study; Final Report September 1998-
http://www.aoa.dhhs.gov/abuse/report/default.htm

New York, Monroe County: PRIDE (http://www.elderrespect.org/aging/elderrespect/)

New York, New York City: Elderly Crime Victims Resource Centre
(http://www.nyc.gov/html/dfta/html/elder_abuse.html)

Social Work Department Standard of Practice (http://depts.washington.edu/swweb)

The National Centre on Elder Abuse http://www.elderabusecenter.org/

The National Elder Abuse Incidence Study; Final Report September 1998
http://www.aoa.dhhs.gov/abuse/report/default.htm

U.S. Administration on Ageing (http://www.aoa.gov/)

Canada

Abuse Education, Prevention and Response Project (http://fp.kwic.com/~jpreston/)

Canada: Access to Justice Network (http://www.acjnet.org/)

Caregiver Network Canada http://www.caregiver.on.ca/

Division of Ageing and Seniors, Population Health Directorate, Health Canada, Address Locator 1908A1, Ottawa, Ontario, KlA 1B4, Telephone: (613) 952-7606, Fax: (613) 957-7627
http://www.hc-sc.gc.ca/seniors-aines/seniors/english/division.htm

The Haldimand and Norfolk Community Response Network http://www.hncrn.ca/

The National Advisory Council on Ageing (Canadian), Ottawa, Ontario, Postal Locator: 1908A1, K1A 1B4, Tel: (613) 957-1968, Fax: (613) 957-9938, Internet address: seniors@hc-sc.gc, http://www.hc-sc.gc.ca/seniors-aines/seniors/english/naca/naca.htm

The Ontario Network for the Prevention of Elder Abuse
(http://www.utoronto.ca/lifecourse/onpea.htm)

Australia

The Aged Rights Advocacy Service (ARAS) www.sa.agedrights.asn.au/ http://www.sa.agedrights.asn.au/prevent/home.html

Carers Australia http://www.carers.asn.au/

Centre for Education & Research on Ageing http://www.cera.usyd.edu.au/index.html

City of Joondalup Elder Protection Network www.elderprotection.net/

Council on Ageing Australia http://www.cota.org.au/

Office for Older Australians, Department of Health and Ageing, Central Office, GPO Box, 9848, Canberra ACT 2601, Australia, Facsimile: 02-6282 4412, Tel 02 6289 1555, http://www.health.gov.au/

New Zealand

Age Concern New Zealand http://www.ageconcern.org.nz

The Health and Disability Commissioner http://www.hdc.org.nz/

Ministry of Health, 133 Molesworth St, P.O. Box 5013, Wellington, New Zealand, Phone: 04 – 496-2000, Fax: 04 – 496-2340, http://www.moh.govt.nz/moh.nsf

The National Health Committee http://www.nhc.govt.nz/

Hong Kong

Elderly Health Service Department, Elderly Health Services Head Office, Room 3502-4, 35th Floor, Hopewell Centre, 183 Queen's Road East, Wan Chai, Hong Kong, Tel: 2121 8621 http://www.info.gov.hk/elderly/english/index.htm

Sample Process for psycho-social assessment of older people when abuse is suspected

Objective: to obtain sufficient information to understand the victim who is at the centre of the investigation; to look at factors from their past and present situation which are helpful in understanding the dynamics of the relationship with the alleged abuser; to get information that is helpful for developing a Care Plan to meet current needs and provide for the future health and welfare of the older person. The scale and depth of the assessment should be kept in proportion to the older person's needs and the level of perceived risk.

The strengths as well as weaknesses of the older person should be identified.

The psycho-social assessment depends on the Senior Case-worker's ability to engage with the older person and develop trust over a period of time. It cannot be developed at one meeting. The psycho-social assessment is not static: it is the assessment of a dynamic between the older person and her environment (including her relationship with a social network) and thus may fluctuate.

Interview the client alone and presume that the client has capacity until evidence proves otherwise. Interviews with family members, including the alleged perpetrator, carers, neighbours and others, as appropriate, should be carried out to get a more complete picture of the older person and their situation. As alleged perpetrators and others close to the older person (and indeed the older person themselves) may present as fearful, angry, upset, or even hostile or intimidating to the Senior Case-worker, it is important that he/she has the skills required to deal with this.

These are the main factors that the Working Group recommend be included in the psychosocial assessment of suspected abuse of an older person.

The older person's social history is helpful in understanding their coping ability and problem-solving strengths.

1. Social History

- Date of birth and place of birth
- Childhood
- Marital history
- Education

- Life changes, including moves
- Occupation, skills-client/spouse
- Hobbies, interests, religious involvement
- History/patterns of violence/abuse in family of origin/marriage/adult life
- How is conflict handled in this family?
- Income: financial difficulties/issues, control over finances and any major decisions
- Accommodation: issues/problems
- How is privacy provided for the older person?

2. Social Networks/Resources

- Living alone/with others: specify
- Significant others; spouse, sibling, children
- Who does the older person believe is her 'closest' relative, friend, and support?
- Who makes decisions for or with the older person?
- With whom is she in regular contact? Frequency/nature of contact
- On whom does the older person depend? For what? Such as shopping, meals and company
- Pattern of communication with significant others
- Available transport
- Social Activities: frequency. What is a routine day/week like for the older person? Opportunities and ability to socialise.

3. Psychological health

The person administering an assessment tool to determine psychological health should have appropriate training. If significant mental health problems are found, referral to the mental health services may be required. Factors that may be significant in assessment of mental health include signs of

- Tense, fearful, angry, low or no affect moods
- Depression/anxiety/moods. Among the tools developed to assess mood are the following:

  (a) Philadelphia Geriatric Centre Morale Scale (Anglicised version, 17 items) (Davis and Challis, 1986) (See Lawton, 1975 for the original version).

  (b) Geriatric Depression Scale (15 items — or the 4 item scale for overview assessment) (Yesavage et al, 1983; Yesavage, 1998).

  (c) BASDEC (Brief Assessment Schedule Depression Cards) (Ashead et al, 1992). Hospital Anxiety Depression Scale (Zigmond and Snaith, 1994).

84

- Post-traumatic stress disorder — re-experience of the trauma through nightmares or intrusive thoughts about the abuse, numbed responsiveness through markedly diminished interest in significant activities, or intensification of symptoms by exposure to events that symbolise the trauma (American Psychiatric Association, 1987).

- Speech — pressured, slow or monosyllabic answers

- Current or past alcohol or substance abuse

- History of psychiatric illness/treatment/hospitalisation

- Shame, humiliation

- Strong ambivalent feelings towards the alleged abuser

- Feelings of hopelessness

- Thought content and form; do the older person's thoughts make sense and proceed to a logical conclusion? Are there themes to the older person's thoughts?

- Actions/statements suggesting mistrust of others. These may have an objective basis.

- Perception of own situation

- Cognitive impairment/Memory/Orientation

Among the tools already developed to assess cognitive impairment are brief mental status questionnaires. These do not give a comprehensive outcome in determining a person's capacity to consent to services in specific situations (Sabatino, Bifocal Article).

- Mini-Mental State Examination (MMSE) (Folstein et al, 1975)

If it is suspected that the carer is stressed, his or her mental health may need to be assessed.

4. Physical Health

- Physical/functional health
- Physical appearance — clothing, hygiene
- Appetite and sleeping patterns
- Presence of bruises or wounds
- Appropriateness of the environment to the older person

Referral for medical examination is necessary if there is suspicion of physical abuse and if mental incapacity is suspected. This may also be necessary to rule out physical causes of confusion owing to problems with medication, infection, vitamin or B12 deficiencies or other treatable conditions.

5. Current Abuse

- Types of abuse
- Severity of abuse
- Frequency of abuse

- Co-operation with the investigation — denies abuse, refuses to co-operate

- Previous history of violence or abuse

It is important to note that assessment of elder abuse is a process that may take time, especially if the older person is in fear and refuses intervention. It is therefore imperative that the Senior Case-Worker keep such cases open and provide appropriate support/services to the older person to increase his/her confidence and empower the older person to accept necessary intervention.

Sample of an appropriate approach to intervention in elder abuse

Once a case of elder abuse has been identified, the next step for the Senior Case-Worker and the team he/she is working with on each case is intervention. Intervention strategies can involve a wide range of services, including: health, social and/or financial services, emotional and physical support, education and counselling, family and respite care, or criminal proceedings.

Any form of intervention must however, where possible, allow the older person to remain in charge of their own life, with the power to decide whether or not they want services, and without the threat of involuntary admission to residential care.

Barriers to intervention

Biggs, Phillipson and Kingston (1995) identified barriers to intervention and cited Penhale (1994) who identified five main issues. These are:

(a)   Older people have the right to self-determination in all aspects of their lives. As a consequence they may refuse offers of help from professional workers.

(b)   Few options exist in terms of proven intervention strategies.

(c)   Workers often respond to these difficulties by lowering their expectations about what can be achieved, especially in situations involving some form of violence or neglect of a long-standing nature.

(d)   The initial assessment may fail for a variety of reasons, to identify the severity of abuse within the domestic or institutional setting.

(e)   Intervention may be an uneasy mix of therapeutic and legal strategies.

Models of intervention

The dynamics and complexity of each individual case of elder abuse means that one model of intervention cannot be applied in individual cases.

Biggs et al. (1995) presents models of intervention with the social work intervention model allowing for varying levels of intervention in the abusive situation. This model shares perspectives, which are also used by healthcare and other professional workers. Integral to this model is the importance of case or care management as a strategy for handling complex problems associated with elder abuse. Care management may be defined as a process of co-ordinating a range of support services and a flexible package of care to meet the assessed needs of the older person and their carer. At all stages it is clear that counselling would be a significant element in any intervention and there is now an emerging discussion on the range of counselling skills appropriate to work with older people.

Stages of intervention

Kingston and Reay (1996) divide intervention into the following stages:

(a) Primary stage — prevention.

(b) Secondary stage — intervention must begin with a comprehensive assessment procedure. A multi-disciplinary approach to assessment should always be adopted, as medical, social and psychological assessments are needed before further action can be decided upon. Booth, Bruno and Marin (1996) argue that the goals of secondary stage of intervention are to treat promptly, to detect abuse early and to minimise morbidity. Crisis management techniques are often utilised during this stage of intervention.

(c) Tertiary stage — includes a programme of support, community care, ongoing therapy where appropriate and ongoing education.

Booth, Bruno and Marin (1996) argue that the aim of tertiary intervention is to engage the victim and perpetrator (if appropriate) of abuse in a treatment process to prevent further abuse and enable optimum recovery. Long-term solutions are to keep monitoring and keep the problem-solving of short-term treatment but add interventions that redress long-term risk factors related to the characteristics of the victim, the perpetrator or family system. With all stages of intervention, professionals must be competent in general supportive therapy skills. More complex therapeutic strategies are needed when the victim or perpetrator denies the significance of abuse or fails to appreciate the behaviours or attitudes that lead to it. Such cases generally require the intervention of mental health professionals with considerable psychotherapy experiences. Individual, interpersonal or family orientated approaches must be considered depending on the circumstances.

References

Baumhover L.A and S.C Beall (eds) (1996) *Abuse Neglect and Exploitation of Older Persons — Strategies for Assessment and Intervention*. London: Jessica Kingsley Publishers.

Biggs S., C. Phillipson and P. Kingston (1995) *Elder Abuse in Perspective* Buckingham, Open University Press.

Booth B.K, A.A. Bruno and R. Marin (1996) 'Psychological therapy with the abused and neglected patient" in L.A Bauhovers and C.S. Beall (1996) *Abuse Neglect and Exploitation of Older Persons — Strategies for Assessment and Intervention*. London: Jessica Kingsley Publishers.

Kingston P, B. Penhale (1994) 'Recognition of a major problem: assessment and management of elder abuse and neglect' *Professional Nurse* 9(5): 343-347.

Woods R.T. (1996) *Handbook of the Clinical Psychology of Ageing* Chichester: John Wiley & Sons.

Kingston P. and A. Reay (1996) 'Elder Abuse And Neglect' in R.T. Woods (1996). *Handbook of the Clinical Psychology of Ageing*, Chichester: John Wiley & Sons

Wt. —. 2,000. 11/02. Cahill. (M70847). G.Spl.